A DOCTOR'S QUICK GUIDE TO HOME TREATMENTS FOR OVER 200 COMMON AILMENTS

A DOCTOR'S QUICK GUIDE
TO HOME TREATMENTS
FOR OVER 200
COMMON AILMENTS

by Jean and Cle Kinney with
Jack Finkelstein, M. D.

PARKER PUBLISHING COMPANY, INC.

West Nyack, N. Y.

Library of Congress
Catalog Card Number: 70-169127

Printed in the United States of America
ISBN 0-13-402172-X
B & P

How This Book Came
to be Written . . . and Why

Last summer, we rented a vacation home on our Connecticut farm to Dr. Jack Finkelstein. All of us swam often in the small lake below our house.

One day I ran up to the house bare-footed from swimming and stubbed my little toe against the leg of a chair. For the next two days I limped around in an old shoe hoping my toe, which had turned purple, would soon recover from its "bruise." On the third morning, I hobbled down to see Jack Finkelstein.

"Dr. Finkelstein . . . ," I began.

"I am mentally buttoning on my white coat," he said. "What can I do for you?"

I showed him my toe. "Should I have this X-rayed?"

He knelt down in the grass and pressed his thumb up against the sole of my foot in the metatarsal region. "Does that hurt?"

WHAT THE DOCTOR WAS TRYING TO FIND OUT

When there is extreme pain in the metatarsal area, the bone is probably broken, and X-rays and an orthopedic specialist are called for. When the pain is confined to just one toe, the trouble is much less serious and can be cared for at home. See Figure A-1 as to how Dr. Finkelstein handled the foot.

WHEN THERE'S NO PAIN IN THE METATARSAL AREA

When the doctor pressed the metatarsal bone, I felt no pain but when he felt along my little toe, I winced.

"There's a break in the toe, only," he said, "so it's easy to fix." Later that morning he taped my little toe to my fourth toe, which served as a splint.

Our secretary looked on with amazement. "My son broke his toe once," she told us, "and, with the X-ray, doctor, a special splint and new slippers, it cost us about 50 dollars." She shook her head. "And to think I could have gotten by with a spool of tape." She turned to the doctor. "Do you suppose my son's break was more serious?"

"The treatment would still be the same," the doctor said. *"Immobilize the toe by taping it to the next one."*

"What if you think the toe is broken but it's only bruised?" my husband asked.

Jack shrugged. "So you tape up a bruised toe."

BIRTH OF A BOOK

In a few days, when I taped my toe, I decided there must be hundreds of such ways to save money on medical care, *if only doctors and pharmacists would open up.* My husband agreed, and we talked to Dr. Finkelstein. "How about doing a money-saving medical book with us?"

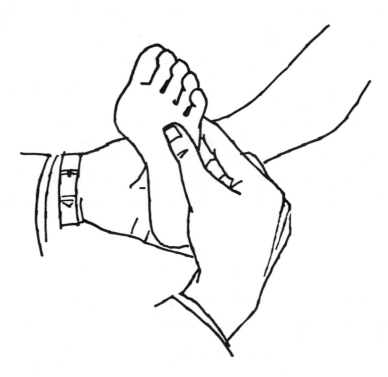

The doctor was thoughtful. "If people knew how to take care of the little things they call a doctor for," he said, "doctors could give more time to the big things." He told us doctors don't want their patients to spend more than they have to for prescriptions, but sometimes "doctors don't *know* the least expensive way to buy." He believed there was a need for the book.

We moved ahead.

A "BRASS TACKS" APPROACH

Our aim was to avoid medical jargon and to take a "brass tacks" approach.

We were determined to make all directions easy to understand, to give the "reason why" for every treatment and to make sure that readers can save money on every recommended drug.

The book contains suggestions for treating more than 200 diseases and/or accidents that can happen to anyone. It is plainly written and can save you money. As you read, we believe you will agree with others who say, "It's about time."

Jean Kinney

What This Book

Can Do for You

This book is unlike any medical book ever written. Based on scientific findings approved by the finest medical minds of the '70s, it helps you to understand the working parts of your body as never before. But it doesn't stop there. As it trains you to see in a matter of minutes when something in your physical make-up is decidedly (or even slightly) off kilter, it tells you how to deal with the problem as the world's top doctors recommend. Then, you will know what to do to straighten out what has gone wrong. Think for a minute what this can mean to you and anyone else whose care is in your hands.

• Vigor and vitality rush back to a depleted body *once disease is thrown off.* Before you can believe it, you feel good again!

• Robust health becomes a way of life when you know how to analyze and get rid of anything that makes for a downbeat condition.

• Frustration about not knowing how to get rid of nagging ailments *that send most people running to a doctor* becomes a thing of the past.

RIGHT AT YOUR FINGERTIPS . . . QUICK REMEDIES AND CURES FOR MORE THAN 200 COMMON AILMENTS

Most of the time, you need no book, you may be saying to yourself, to tell you what's the matter. Your trouble is one that you've had to learn to live with. Year after year, you suffer the stress of constipation, arthritis, bleeding gums, dandruff, recurring headaches or whatever, and you've survived. Still, if you had the money and the time to leave tomorrow for a world-renowned clinic with specialists who could permanently eliminate the cause of your persistent discomfort or embarrassment, wouldn't you take off in the morning? With all the bother you've been through, you would be the first one on the plane. Happily, what you are going to find as you go through these pages is that you don't have to head for the airport. The answers that you have been looking for are all right here.

On page after page, you will find descriptions of one ailment after another up to 200 or more that constantly take away from the ability of thousands, even millions, of human beings to enjoy life to its fullest. The causes of kidney disturbances, constant coughing, vaginal discharges, pimples, night sweats, stiff neck— even the desire to masturbate—and dozens of far more complicated problems are discussed in simple terms. What to do about anything that is troubling you is set forth with all the clarity of a "Dick and Jane" book. There is no medical jargon. Even when the problem is a complicated one, you will understand every single word.

CUTS THROUGH MEDICAL JARGON—GETS DOWN TO BASICS

Often, when you go to a doctor, who for many years has been pouring over textbooks filled with technical explanations, scientific procedures and all the six syllable pharmaceutical names for drugs, you can't tell what he's talking about. Here, all the gobbledygook is thrown out the window and explanations and directions are set forth so that a child can understand. Yet, nowhere in the book is there a *sacrifice of scientific truth.* You get the best help that modern medicine can offer—*with amazing results!*

Wouldn't you like to be free from the annoying sinus condition that makes it so hard for you to breathe? Or find a way to smooth out those ugly wrinkles that make you look old before your time? Or get relief from the nagging backache that makes getting out of bed sheer agony on some mornings?

Now, in this book, you can look in the automatic reference section (quick-indexed so you won't waste a moment) and see exactly what to do without fuss or bother. In each case, by the time you've finished with the what-to-do paragraph, you will be on your way to long-lasting relief.

DOCTOR-TESTED AND APPROVED

We've packed this encyclopedia with valuable medical information, all doctor-tested and approved. You will find simple methods for giving the best medical care to your family in case of sudden illness or injury . . . quick relief cures for 15 types of baby illnesses including colic, colds and skin problems . . . remedies that conquer 40 childhood problems . . . a six-step therapy program for ridding yourself of insomnia . . . and if you are plagued with unsightly varicose veins, you'll want to check the section that has helped hundreds and thousands end this problem for good.

FAST RELIEF FROM PRACTICALLY ANYTHING THAT AILS YOU

One vital part of the book tells you how to get fast relief from pains caused by nervous tension, overeating, the 24-hour virus and even motion sickness. In other sections, you will discover the best cure for hardening of the arteries, how to relieve the agony of arthritis and bursitis, how to live without fear with diabetes, how to get relief from foot problems before you can believe it and how to get the most effective health aid in the world absolutely free!

HELPS YOU LIKE AN "INSTANT HOSPITAL"

Because this book shows you how your body works and explains the causes of your aches and pains, you won't be running to the doctor or hurrying to the drug store for expensive pills whenever you don't feel right. Not now, when you'll have beside you at all times your own "instant hospital."

Read through one section alone and you will come away with a complete understanding of the digestive system, urinary system, blood vessels, heart, brain, bones, senses—everything a medical student has to know as he prepares to be a doctor. Read through another, and you will know what is in any prescription you are told to buy and why it is being prescribed. Read what to do in case of an accident or sudden illness and you will stay calm and effective in any emergency.

Perhaps, you will read the book straight through and pick up useful health hints, or you may keep it close at hand for quick help when a special problem comes along. Either way your "instant hospital" will be a godsend. The book will save you worry, but it can also save you hours of time in a doctor's office or outpatient clinic and, of course, it can save you money. In this day of spiraling medical and hospital costs, dollars spent for medical care can cripple a family forever. Still, important as they are, time and money are not the main reasons for keeping this book within reach. By helping you to find your personal key to better health, the book points the way to a happier life. Once your vitality is not drained away by infection or illness, every day will have a meaning it never had before.

Jean Kinney
Cle Kinney
Jack Finkelstein, M.D.

Nine Built-In Benefits
That Come With This Book

1. *Immediate Relief.* Pains disappear; all discomfort caused by many types of illness vanishes when you follow the tested formulas and programs of this book.
2. *Robust health.* Easy recipes can actually transform a sickly person into one blessed with perfect health.
3. *New resistance to disease.* Never again need you or yours be afraid of catching most of the contagious diseases that are going around. Even the casual reader can find ways to fend off illness and stay protected from germs.
4. *Vigor and vitality.* You'll see how a lost feeling of energy comes back to a body that seemed forever tired. Goodbye to "sad sack" days!
5. *Long lasting.* The cures in this book are not fleeting ones. Relief comes in most cases for months, years, *even permanently.*
6. *Look and feel young again.* Wrinkles smooth out and your eyes and face take on a new glow no matter how old you are! You'll find yourself moving around with the agility of someone far younger.
7. *Safe and easy.* The treatments in this book are not complicated and call for no drugs not recommended by doctors. Each can be performed whenever and wherever needed with a complete feeling of security.
8. *Shed unwanted pounds quickly without drugs.* Step-by-step directions show you how to lose 10, 20, 30 pounds or more using tested methods prescribed by medical scientists with years and years of training.
9. *Save money.* Going to doctors for minor illnesses now becomes a thing of the past. Prescription costs can be cut way down in spite of inflation. Best of all, the book shows you how to give hospital-type care right in your own home.

Contents

How This Book Came to be Written . . . and Why . 5

What This Book Can Do for You . 9

Nine Built-In Benefits That Come With This Book . 13

PART ONE

Foolproof Ways to Save Hundreds of Dollars
On Drugs and Other Supplies

*1 .   Seven Low Cost Remedies to Relieve Dozens
of Nuisance Ailments . 21*

*Everyday Health Aids . Seven Low-Cost Aids . Now Try This
Experiment*

*2   Today's 21 "Most Used" Drugs and Why Your Doctor
Prescribes Each One . 35*

How to Use This Information . The Time to Pay Attention .
16 Common Reasons to Consult a Doctor . Twenty-One U.S.P.
Drugs Prescribed Over and Over by Doctors

*3   A Five-Step Formula for Cutting the Cost of Every
Pill or Prescription You Buy . 45*

A Time for Tact . It Will Pay You to Ask for the Generic Drug .
Learn to See Through TV Commercials and Publicity "Plants" .
Nature's Best Blender . How to Be Prepared for Simple Emergencies

PART TWO

Descriptions of More Than 200 Everyday
Illnesses and Injuries and What to do for Each One

*4   When Your Baby is New: How to Avoid Big Spending
Without Being Neglectful . 53*

15

4   When Your Baby is New: How to Avoid Big Spending
     Without Being Neglectful (*Con't*)

     Five Ways to Save Money During the Baby's First Year . Quick
     Relief for 15 Types of Upsets

5   *What to Do for a Child When Trouble Comes Suddenly . 61*

     When a Cut is Deep . How to Be a Detective When Your Baby
     is Seriously Ill

6   *How to Cope with 40 Childhood Problems that
     are Bound to Cause Worry . 67*

     Birthmark or Cyst . Blood in Urine, Feces or Vomit . Broncho-
     pneumonia . Car Sickness . Chicken Pox . Diarrhea . Diptheria
     Dog Bite . Ear Problems, including Deafness, Earache, Mastoid .
     Eczema . Emotional Disturbances . Eye Problems, including In-
     juries, Eyelid and seeing Problems . Food Allergy . Head Lice .
     Heart Murmer . Hernia . Influenza . Measles . Meningitis .
     Poison Ivy . Poisoning from Aspirin, Crayons, Paints, Glue or
     Anything Else . Rheumatic Fever . Roseola Infantum . Scarlet
     Fever . Sinusitis . Smashed Finger . Smegna . Stomach-Ache .
     Streptococcus Infection . Sunburn . Swallowing of Sharp Object
     . Swollen Glands . Thrush . Tonsillitis or Enlarged Adenoids .
     Too Fat or Too Thin . Tooth Decay . Vomiting . Warts .
     Whooping Cough . Worms . Don't Be An Over-Anxious Parent

7   *How to Deal With Accidents and 31 Diseases that Occur
     in Adolescence . 89*

     Seven Emergencies Every Young Person Should Know How to Deal
     With . When Mouth to Mouth Respiration is Impossible . 31
     Problems in Addition to Accidents . What to Do When a Stricken
     Person Can't Talk

8   *133 Get Well Recipes for Adults
     Who Are Injured or Ill . 107*

     Number One Killer, Motor Vehicle Accident . Number Two Killer,
     Falls . Number Three Killer, Burns . Number Four Killer, Drowning .
     Number Five Killer, Firearms . Number Six Killer, Machinery .
     Number Seven Killer, Poison Gases . Number Eight Killer, Internal
     Poisons . How to Bring Back Someone Who is Almost Gone .
     Mental Attitude Can Bring Relief . How to Give Heart Massage

PART THREE

How to Save Up to 90 Percent When You Have Medical Care

9   *Foolproof Ways to Avoid Money-Wasting Traps
When You Have a Chronic Problem . 183*

How to Proceed When You Suspect a Chronic Disease

10   *Five Sure-Fire Money-Saving Rules the
Average Person Never Considers . 187*

11   *Where to Go for Special Services Your
Taxes Help to Support . 197*

What If You Can Afford to Pay? . Many Diagnostic Services Are Free . Why the Government Wants You to Have These Free Examinations . Other Free Services . Depend On Your Local Visiting Nurse Association . There is More Help Than You Know

12   *101 Places to Get Free Medical Information That Can Save
You Thousands of Dollars . 205*

101 Associations . Three Hundred Years Ago These Arm Experiments Led to the Discovery of Blood Circulation

PART FOUR

How Your Body Functions

13   *Simplified Explanations of 11 Body Systems . 217*

Your Skin: The Protective Envelope That Covers Your Body For Fuel and Growth: The Digestive System . For Purification: The Urinary System . To Help Produce Energy; Your Respiratory System . Piepline for Your Blood: Your Blood Vessels and Heart . For Your Overall Protection: The Lymphatic System . For Communication: Your Brain and Nerves . The Special Senses: Hearing, Tasting, Seeing, Smelling . For Support and Motion: Your Bones. Muscles and Connective Tissue . For Regulation: The Endocrine Glands . For Transmitting Life: The Reproductive System

PART FIVE

Simple "Stay Well" Recipes for Everyone At Your House

14   *How to Avoid Medical Expense All Along the Way . 235*

15   *Health Robbers to be Avoided All Along the Way . 239*

16   *Three Vital D's That Make for Well-Being: Diet, Deep-Breathing and Delight in Life* . *243*

If You Are Overweight . Deep-Breathing . Delight in Life

Bibliography . *247*

Index . *249*

A DOCTOR'S QUICK GUIDE TO HOME TREATMENTS FOR OVER 200 COMMON AILMENTS

PART ONE

Foolproof Ways to Save Hundreds of Dollars on Drugs and Other Supplies

1

Seven Low Cost Remedies to Relieve Dozens of Nuisance Ailments

The most important health aid in your home is one that you scarcely notice because it is always there, *water*. Consider briefly the many ways in which your family may be called upon to use this liquid compound of hydrogen and oxygen in one week (or even in one day) and you will see that no medicinal mixture ever concocted has the therapeutic power and versatility of H_2O.

You would be arrested if you were to bottle plain water and sell it as a medicine, yet you use it over and over as a "medicine" all the time. Here are 21 ways:

1. As a daily replenishment for water lost in urine, the feces, perspiration and in moisture exhaled from the lungs.
2. As a swallowing aid (i.e., to wash down chewable tablets) and as a holding agent in the stomach. (Unlike a tablet chewed without water which may be discharged immediately into the small intestine, powders, liquids or tablets dissolved in water stay longer in the stomach.)
3. As a solvent (i.e., for a beef bouillon cube when you're taking this for extra protein).

4. As an eyewash for irritated eyes. (Try two or three drops of clean tap water on the lower lid to clear away smog irritation.)
5. As a wetting agent for an ice cold compress for tired eyes. (A soft cloth wet with ice water relieves "tired eyes" in 15 minutes.)
6. To carry away excess oil from scalp, hair and skin.
7. As a wetting agent (when heated) for a hot compress to encourage drainage from a pimple.
8. As a cleanser for a small cut.
9. As a sterilizer (when boiled) for the needle you will use to remove a splinter.
10. As an astringent to stop surface bleeding (i.e., bathroom tissue wet with cold water stanches blood from a razor nick in seconds).
11. In a cold compress.
12. Warmed (with salt as a saline gargle) for sore throat.
13. For use in contrast baths (first, hot; then, cold) to relieve tired feet.
14. For a douche, as prescribed.
15. For an enema, as prescribed.
16. In an ice bag (when frozen and crushed) to relieve pain or inflammation.
17. Heated to a temperature of 130° for use in a hot water bag.
18. Inhaled as a steamy vapor to relieve sinusitis or other congestion.
19. Placed on the skin with a layer of vaseline over it for dry skin.
20. With soap as a germicide.
21. To swim in order to relax muscles, exercise stiff joints and for other health reasons.

You can name a dozen other therapeutic uses for water without half trying, if you want to make a game of it, but that is not the purpose of this listing. We are simply reminding you of your dependence on water to help you understand that (1) the best cure is often the simplest; (2) the most effective remedy need not be costly. With this in mind, let's stock your medicine shelf with seven products that will relieve almost anything—and will cost over a period of a year no more than a few dollars.

EVERYDAY HEALTH AIDS

If you could have only seven health aids outside of water to take care of anything that might happen to you and your family, wherever you may be, what would you put in your bathroom? (This is not a game, trick question or a joke and does not include towels, toilet tissue, toothpaste and cosmetics.) We refer here to the special products you will need to treat yourself, a guest or another member of the family for any minor ailment or accident that may occur on any day. The containers, unlabelled, are set out in Figure 1-1.

Figure 1: Unlabelled containers for the basic 7 health aids that should be in your home. Can you supply the names of the contents?

Can you identify the seven low-cost products shown here that will take care of the average family's nuisance ailments?

The seven basic products listed in this chapter can be purchased without a prescription and all can be asked for by their *generic* name, not by their trade advertised name, permitting any reasonably well-informed buyer to make a choice of brands and thus save 15, 30, even 50% or more on any given item without sacrificing quality, purity or potency. Read down the list of items, the suggested uses for each one and the money-saving way to buy each for less.

SEVEN LOW-COST AIDS

Here are the seven versatile products that will help you through almost any emergency that you can think of and easy directions for buying each one for less.

1. *Soap*

   How soap works: Every molecule in soap has two parts, one dissolving in oil, the other in water. Thus, any ordinary soap (1) breaks up the invisible layer of "fat" that holds dirt (and germs) on the skin and (2) helps water to carry it away. A synthetic detergent works in the same way.

   When first introduced, synthetics were acclaimed for leaving no scum (undissolved calcium and magnesium salts) in the bathtub and on the skin; but were criticized by rival soaps for over-stripping or "burning." Today, finely milled soaps leave little scum; few detergents "burn." There is little difference in the overall action.

   Uses: You use toilet soap (or a synthetic detergent) to wash your hands and face and for the bath. But to keep you looking and feeling clean is not soap's only purpose.

   Second to water, soap (real or synthetic) is indicated more often than any other product as a therapeutic agent in home and hospital "medical books." Here are a few of its uses:

   > *As an antiseptic:* Use warm soapy water to wash out a dog bite, to wash the skin around a puncture wound, to wash out wounds and scratches, to clean skin before removing a splinter. Use it anytime, in fact, to prevent infection when the skin has been accidentally cut. (Before operating, a surgeon scrubs his hands with *soap and water* for 10 minutes to rid them of germs before donning surgical gloves.)

To prevent the intake of germs: Wash hands before eating to avoid ingesting bacteria, viruses or protozoa which may be in dirt.

Step one in ridding skin of acne: Scrub face, chest and back with plain soap and fairly hot water to remove fatty deposits left in pores by overactive sebaceous glands.

To wash away dandruff flakes: Use dissolved soap and water as a shampoo; it washes oil and flakes from the hair just as it gets rid of excess oil on the skin.

As a lubricant: Add soap to warm water in an enema bag so that stool can be easily passed.

Because of its dozens of therapeutic uses, soap belongs in your medicine chest or kit at all times.

To get the best soap or detergent for the least possible money, get the soap with the fewest perfumes, creams and other non-essential additives in the brand that costs the least. In making your selection, avoid these errors in thinking:

Floating soap is always pure. (Not necessarily, although the converse is not true, either. To make floating soap, air is injected into molten soap during the manufacturing process so that the final bar is less dense than water.)

Antibacterial agents in soap cleanse away germs left behind by ordinary soap. (Not so, because soap, itself, is a disinfectant and all but an infinitesimal amount is washed away, anyway. However, antibacterial soap used consistently may leave a slight film that reduces surface bacteria in some infinitesimal degree and thus leaves a little less bacteria on the skin to work its way down into follicles. Such soaps cleanse no more "deeply" than ordinary soaps, however, and are no more effective on a "one shot" antiseptic basis than any good soap.)

Expensive "medicated soaps" are disease preventatives for the entire family. (They are germicides as all soaps are germicides, but they are "medicated" by little more than being infused with borax or carbolic acid or some other additive during the manufacturing process. Read the label so that you know what additive you are paying for before you buy. Then, buy only if your skin condition requires some. Otherwise, you are paying for something that was added for a promotion reason rather than for medication.)

To buy soap for less: (1) Buy the "loss leader" advertised at a discount store or supermarket; (2) buy in quantity; (3) don't pay for cosmetic or medicated "extras;" (4) don't buy "10¢ Off" or other offers without checking price against other soaps.

2. *Aspirin*

A true wonder drug: In 1893, acetylsalicylic acid was isolated from a dye waste product and given the trade name Aspirin by Hermann Dreser, a staff chemist at the Bayer Dye Works in Germany.[1] It is a true wonder drug. Far less expensive than quinine, it is equally effective as a fever-reducer. Less irritating when taken internally than oil of wintergreen, it is a far more effective pain-reliever than the old remedy. And it has other uses, as noted below.

Uses for aspirin:

To relieve cold symptoms: Take one or two tablets every two or three hours to relieve headache, sore throat and sniffles.

To reduce fever (in adults or children): Sore throat and a high fever come as a result of a cold or local infection. And sometimes a fever comes from other causes. Aspirin, in such cases, brings body temperature down to normal. (For children: no more than 1 grain (60 mgm) of aspirin for every year of age every 3 to 4 hours, and no more often than 3 times a day for 2 days. To help you figure: the average aspirin tablet contains 5 grains, so a 2-1/2-year-old child can take 1/2 a tablet. Be very cautious about giving aspirin to a child under two.) When fever is high, excessive perspiration causes dehydration. To counteract, take plenty of liquids along with aspirin.

To suppress inflammation in arthritic joints: Aspirin reduces swelling, relieves pain, makes it easier to move joints, which is in itself a benefit.

As a pain reliever: Take aspirin for painful arthritis, rheumatism, muscle aches of all kinds, tension headaches.

Aspirin is relatively harmless unless you happen to be allergic to it, in which case it can produce hives or some other discomfort. If so, avoid aspirin in any product. (The base of all of the usual pain and fever-reducing products, such as Bufferin, Anacin, Alka-Seltzer, Empirin, Excedrin, etc., is aspirin, so if aspirin produces an allergic reaction in one form, it will produce it in another.)

If your stomach seems to be upset by aspirin, take the tablets along with plenty of water or after a meal. If you still feel your stomach is upset by aspirin, take aspirin along with an antacid. It is not necessary to pay extra for antacid tablets (or for Bufferin or Alka-Seltzer which are so-called "soft" aspirin products so break up fast in the stomach and contain a small amount of antacid). Take a teaspoon of inexpensive bicarbonate of soda along with your aspirin for a similar buffering effect.

Do not pay extra for candy-flavored aspirin. Most children have no difficulty in swallowing regular aspirin. If yours finds this difficult, give a half or a quarter of an aspirin tablet in a spoonful of honey, molasses or maple syrup. An over-dosage of aspirin can be harmful to a child, and candy aspirin is attractive.

To buy aspirin for less: (1) Buy the least expensive brand of aspirin, so labeled, that you can buy. (Look on the bottle for the initials, U.S.P.[2]) Anything labeled Aspirin, U.S.P., is exactly like any other aspirin and like all the aspirin included in Anacin, Bufferin or any other aspirin-based product. (2) Buy at a discount drug store. (3) Do not buy a product with an additional ingredient or two which is nothing more than "glorified aspirin." (4) Buy no more aspirin than you will use in two or three months, and keep cap on tight. (Aspirin decomposes, crumbles easily, has a vinegar-like odor after

several months; may be more irritating and less effective
when this happens.) (5) When you are tempted to buy a new
drug or compound for a specific reason, check to see
whether aspirin is an ingredient. If so, and the reason for
your purchase is an *aspirin* reason, stick to the real thing.
The highly advertised "compound" will do little more for
you than basic aspirin, and the price will be far higher.

3. *Milk of Magnesia* (U.S.P.)
   Definition: A milky white suspension in water of magnesium
   hydroxide, Mg(OH)2.
   Uses:

> *As a laxative:* Occasionally, when your family is travel-
> ing and eating foods which are different from what you
> ordinarily serve, someone in the group may be tempo-
> rarily constipated. Also, visitors in the home can inter-
> rupt an individual's routine bathroom habits, and/or
> stress can make for constipation. In such cases, a mild
> laxative may be called for. Milk of magnesia is mild, yet
> produces the bowel movement which is desired. (Some-
> times, worry about not having a bowel movement can
> aggravate the nervousness which may have led to the
> constipation in the first place.)
>
> *As an antacid:* To relieve gas, belching, slight nausea or
> sour stomach, take 1/3 of what is suggested to relieve
> constipation.

Milk of magnesia (or any laxative or antacid) should not be
taken habitually. The underlying cause for either condition
should be evaluated if chronic, and even a mild laxative can
encourage rather than alleviate the problem. But when
needed, this one is on the U.S.P. list ana must by law be
manufactured as specified in the approved formula. This, of
course, can save you money.

To save money on milk of magnesia: (1) Buy in liquid form.
(2) Buy milk of magnesia as you do aspirin; do not pay more
for a brand name. (Remember, with U.S.P., the formula
must be identical.) (3) Buy in a discount store *if* generic-
name drugs are sold in this store. However, do not buy a

brand name at a discount store, believing you are paying the lowest possible price. True, you may be paying less than you might have to pay for this same *brand* in a drug store, but you still will be paying for advertising and promotion of that brand name. When you buy by generic name, you pay far less.

4. *Glycerin suppositories* (adult size)[3]

Where glycerin comes from: During the saponification process (in soap-making), colorless, odorless glycerin is formed in addition to soap.

How the suppository works: A glycerin stick, inserted in the rectum, melts and moistens the hard stool, thus stimulating evacuation. It also lubricates the anal passage, thus making an uncomfortable evacuation less painful.

When to use: A glycerin suppository may be all that is needed when constipation is obviously due to stoppage in the anal canal. To push waste with a laxative through 25 feet of the intestine is really silly when all the trouble is in the last few inches. Suppositories like laxatives should not be relied on constantly. Result of constant use can be a disturbance to the mucous membrane of the anal canal.

To buy glycerin suppositories for less: (1) Buy at two-for-one sales (suppositories keep indefinitely when temperature is below 75°; can be refrigerated when temperature mounts); (2) look for least expensive suppository when you shop or as a "loss leader" at any discount drug store; glycerin is glycerin.

5 *Bicarbonate of soda* (U.S.P.)

Definition: $NaCO_3$ is just plain baking soda.

Uses. Good old-fashioned baking soda with its U.S.P. symbol of integrity has almost as many "medicinal" uses as aspirin. Here are the most important:-

> *To relieve pain of minor (first degree) burn:* Apply cool paste of baking soda and cold water to reddened area.
> *As an antacid:* For a mildly upset stomach, take half a teaspoon of soda in a glass of water or fruit juice. "Burp" usually results, brings relief. (Like aspirin, soda

should not be taken day after day, week after week, without consultation with a doctor. Long-time, over-usage of soda can cause kidney problems and "sour stomach", can be a symptom of a deeper problem.)

Along with aspirin: If aspirin, taken for a cold, brings on stomach upset, take soda in one of the liquids you are drinking. This "buffers" aspirin, is less expensive solution to upset stomach problem than Bufferin.

For insect bite: Mix soda with cold cream; apply to raised place. (Remove stinger, in case of bee sting.)

For hives or itching caused by allergy: Bathe in bath water which contains a cupful of soda.

To check excessive perspiration: Dust armpits and feet with soda.

To clean teeth: Mix half teaspoonful of soda with same amount of salt in glass of warm water. Use as "cleaner" for teeth or dentrifice or as a mouth wash.

To buy soda for less: Like aspirin and/or milk of magnesia made according to the original formula approved by U.S.P., any brand of sodium bicarbonate does what any other brand will do. Buy at the supermarket where you get the best buys.

6 *Adhesive bandages*

Purpose: To keep minor skin injury covered with plain white gauze so that dirt is excluded and the wound is guarded against secondary infection. (Plain gauze plus tape is fine, but is less convenient than band-aid type bandage.)

Warnings: (1) Never cover skin break with plain adhesive tape. (Bacteria-attracting moisture becomes trapped under tape, scraped place becomes breeding place for infection.) (2) Get perforated tape which permits air to come through gauze. (3) Do not buy bandages tinted with medicine. (One or more members of your family may be allergic to the medication.)

Uses for adhesive bandages:

For a minor scrape or cut: Apply bandage after clean-ing wound with cool running water and cleansing wound and skin around cut with soap and water. (Blot up water on skin with bathroom tissue so that tape will adhere.) Change bandage daily to keep wound clean.

For a second degree burn: If blistering occurs, wash gently with soap and water and cover with bandage. This will prevent further injury as well as reduce infection possibility.

Bee sting: After removing stinger and coating with baking soda paste, cover with bandage to inhibit scratching when the victim is a child.

How and where to buy for less: (1) Watch for a special sale. (2) Check the brand and number of bandages (listed on the container) against price; buy the size container that gives the most bandages for the least money. (3) As a rule, go to a chain drug or variety store.

7. *Antihistamine tablets*

Definition: A neutralizer to offset the effect of histamine formed in body tissue which produces an allergic reaction. (Some families are allergy-prone; others can find few members who are now or ever have been bothered by hay fever, hives and other allergies.) If you have an allergy-prone family, antihistamine can bring relief to members with many symptoms. If not, you may find an antihistamine tablet of use occasionally for sinus and nasal passage congestion.

Warnings: Children under 6 should not be given an antihistamine without a doctor's recommendation, and those from 6 to 12 should be given only half of an adult dose. Adults taking antihistamines should avoid driving a car or working near machinery because drowsiness is a side effect in most cases.

Recommended uses:

For relief of hay fever symptoms: Take antihistamine as directed during pollen season. (Remember, an antihistamine controls only the symptoms; the basic causes of the condition and possible hay fever "cures" will be discussed in a later chapter.)

For relief of allergic rhinitis: Take as directed when an

attack is brought on (in any season) from house dust, feathers, animal hair, etc.

For help in suppressing cold symptoms: Antihistamines have no effect on the course of a cold but can help to dry up nasal passages and relieve sore throat caused by post nasal drip *if* there is an allergy involvement.

Side effects: (1) Helps patient sleep. (Because most antihistamine compounds tend to make the patient drowsy, one tablet at bedtime can help the patient "get a good night's sleep."[4] This somnolence factor is not a benefit in the daytime if the taker is working with machinery, so this kind of activity should be avoided during treatment.) (2) Some antihistamine compounds prevent car sickness and sea sickness and tend to lessen nausea and diarrhea. (3) A few antihistamines relieve itch, especially as related to hives. (However, no antihistamine should be given for just any itch problem. Itching that accompanies chicken pox, for instance, is not caused by an allergy and will not be helped by antihistamine.)

Note: Some antihistamines are less apt to cause drowsiness than others; some have no anti-nausea effect; others are not effective against car sickness. Most over-the-counter antihistamine tablets contain (a) Chlorpheniramine Maleate, U.S.P., a potent antihistamine which is less likely than some to cause drowsiness and is not effective against motion sickness, or (b) Diphenhydramine Hydrochloride, U.S.P., which is the basis of most motion sickness pills.

If you have an allergy-type cold and are staying sensibly in bed for a couple of days, the letter "a" tablet is for you. If you have hay fever and have a long trip ahead of you, the "b" tablet is better.

How to get what you want and save money, too: Check when you buy any name brand for the basic ingredient (printed on the bottle) or write the generic name of the U.S.P. tablet you want and ask your pharmacist to give you the least expensive brand in the store.

Here are the seven basic "medicines" as labelled in Figure 1-2 that belong on your home medical shelf which should be installed high on the wall of your bathroom where it is easily available but out of the reach of small children. These few products contain all of the medical "ingredients" that are sold in 99 percent of today's highly touted over-the-counter medicines for which American drug companies spend for advertising, alone, a total of $700 million a year. You need no other medical staples in your home.

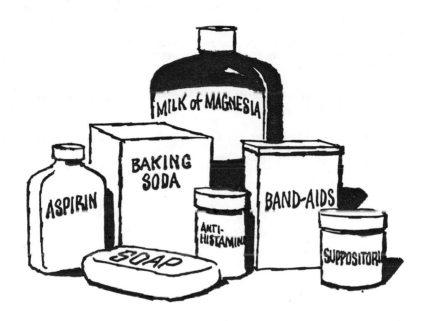

Figure 1-2.

NOW TRY THIS EXPERIMENT

Stock your shelf as advised with the seven named products *and no others*. Then, write down the date. For the following month make a note each time you use a product from your shelf. The first month you may not use any product or you may use all. So extend your time a month. At the end of the year, you will see what products you have used and why. If you buy no other "drugs," you will smile to yourself as you think of how you resisted America's best merchandising minds who may formerly have had you "hooked."

[1]Until World War I, aspirin was the trademark of the Bayer Company but is now public property in the United States and is manufactured by the Rexall Chemical Company, Dow Chemical Company, Miles Laboratories, Inc., Sterling Drug, Inc., Monsanto Company, Norwich Pharmaceutical Company, no others. (Any other company listed on the bottle is simply a distributor; these listed companies are the only American manufacturers.)

[2]The Pharmacopoeia of the United States, a handbook published since 1820 at 10-year intervals (until recently, when it began to be published at five-year intervals) lists drugs *by their generic name* which have specific medical and pharmaceutical standards of strength, quality and purity. It is non-profit, lists no mixtures or combinations of drugs, bases its decisions on a scientific fact. Any drug included in U.S.P. is made according to a specific formula; therefore, any drug sold by any American distributor is manufactured according to this formula.

[3]Suppositories for children can cause tears in the rectum; should not be used. They should not be used regularly by adults.

[4]The basis for almost all of the over-the-counter "sleeping pills" is an antihistamine.

2

Today's 21 "Most Used" Drugs and Why Your Doctor Prescribes Each One

(Prices in this chapter have been verified by a registered pharmacist. Later, some may change, but the money-saving principle will remain the same. Because some drug stores take a much higher mark-up than others, the consumer can save money by doing comparison shopping.)

The 21 drugs described in this chapter are prescribed for more than 90 percent of all disorders that send men, women and children into doctors' offices. Almost without exception, the doctor doing the prescribing has a two-fold aim: to relieve the patient's discomfort with the most effective drug which is also the least likely to produce negative side effects. All of the drugs listed here are manufactured by more than one company and sold, in most cases, under many different brand names. The purpose for their being included here is to acquaint you with the *generic* name for the basic drug in a doctor's prescription which you may be called upon to have filled.[1]

HOW TO USE THIS INFORMATION

There are two ways in which you can benefit from the information in this chapter. (1) Knowing before going to your doctor's office what he is likely to prescribe will make it possible for you to request that his prescription be written for a drug under its generic, not its brand, name. (2) Knowing why a given drug has been prescribed will help you to select a brand in a drug store or department store which costs far less than the high-priced brand the pharmacist may first suggest.

THE TIME TO PAY ATTENTION

Let's say that you have a urinary tract infection and that your doctor writes out a prescription that looks like this, and tells you to take eight tablets a day. Note a typical prescription in Figure 2-1.

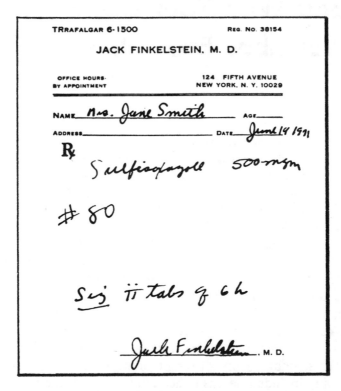

Figure 2-1: Example of a prescription for urinary tract infection.

Having found in this book that the drug usually prescribed for a urinary tract infection is Sulfisoxazole, U.S.P., you look for this on the prescription your doctor writes out for you. This is the moment of truth. If it looks like the above, so far so good, but should your doctor write down Gantrisin or Entrusil, both well-promoted versions of Sulfisoxazole, U.S.P., you are on your way to paying more. It is our opinion that almost without exception any doctor you go to would like to know, but may not know, the price of any drug he prescribes. If apprised of the difference in the price of two brands, he will readily cooperate by prescribing the one that costs the least.[2]

Should you see on the prescription what appears to be a brand name, you can ask your doctor if this is true and what basic generic drug he is recommending. If he says "Sulfisoxazole," as you have anticipated, ask him to write the prescription for that if he doesn't mind. Then, when you get to the discount pharmacy or mail order drug house, ask for or order the least expensive version of the U.S.P. drug you have been advised to buy. Usually, you will be able to buy one at a fraction of the cost of the more highly promoted brands, and when you're taking eight tablets a day, this can mean a real savings.

Go past your moment of truth in the doctor's office, and you are well on your way to paying more. In all but a few states, pharmacists are required by law to sell the brand name recommended by the doctor, even though they may have other less expensive brands on hand that supply the same basic ingredients. There is no law, however, that says you cannot call your doctor after talking with your pharmacist.

When your pharmacist checks your prescription, ask him whether you are buying a brand or generic name. If he says "brand," ask him what basic drug is in your prescription and if he has other less expensive "brands." Then, call from the drug store and tell your doctor that the difference between two brands is substantial and ask if the second brand can do as well. If he tells you that there are other ingredients in the pill he wants you to have or if he says that other manufacturers do not have the same "quality control," you can be sure that he has been oversold by a drug company representative or advertisement in a medical journal the same way that you can be oversold on a dandruff rinse or mouth wash

To avoid an awkward situation, buy for one time as directed, but if your doctor continues to prescribe only high-priced brands rather than generic drugs which have the identical ingredients, you should consider changing doctors.

Most doctors recognize that the state of a man's pocketbook is often a major factor in his concern about a health problem and will modify a prescription as suggested. So, if your doctor will not cooperate, this will be an exceptional case. The average professional man or woman will work with you once you tell him what you're after.

16 COMMON REASONS TO CONSULT A DOCTOR

Other than after an accident (for a burn, cut, break, etc.), the average outpatient who has a prescription filled has consulted a doctor for one of these reasons, which we are listing alphabetically:

1. *Asthma*
2. *Birth control* suggestions
3. *Bladder* infection
4. Pain in *chest*
5. Severe *cold*
6. *Diabetes*
7. *Hemorrhoids,* piles or other discomfort often associated with constipation
8. For a problem associated with *high blood pressure* (dizziness, headache, heart palpitations, etc.)
9. *Menopausal* distress
10. Some problem associated with *nervous* strain (tension headache, tightness of chest muscles, insomnia, extreme menstrual distress, etc.)
11. For help in *reducing*
12. *Rheumatism* or arthritis
13. *Run-down* feeling, constant fatigue
14. *Skin* problems
15. *Stomach* and/or gastrointestinal distress (complaint may be nausea, cramps, motion sickness or something else)
16. Sore *throat*

For any one of these conditions, a drug may be prescribed. Twenty-one of the drugs most often prescribed for one or more of these conditions are listed below.

TWENTY-ONE U.S.P. DRUGS
PRESCRIBED OVER AND OVER BY DOCTORS[3]

1. Belladonna Tincture, U.S.P.
   This old-fashioned aid reduces hydrochloric acid in the

stomach and helps to relax muscles in the gastrointestinal tract. Many doctors still prescribe this for gastrointestinal disorders including peptic ulcer.

This is an inexpensive remedy, sold to your druggist by the bottle. When sold in tablet form, it costs 10 to 20 times as much. Buy in liquid form.

2. Decavitamin Capsules (or tablets), U.S.P.

The only U.S.P. preparation containing multiple vitamins, listed in United States Pharmacopeia, because each vitamin in the capsule or tablet is present in the exact amount recommended as the daily dietary allowance by the National Academy of Sciences-National Research Council.

Price to your druggist for 1,000 tablets ranges from $6 or $7 to close to twice that much for the same formula.[4]

3. Dextroamphetamine Sulfate, U.S.P.—as an appetite suppressant[5]

Sometimes prescribed in a 5 milligram dosage with phenobarbital (15 mg.) to be taken 3 hours before the day's largest meal. The purpose of the Dextroamphetamine is to suppress appetite; of the phenobarbital, to eliminate the nervousness which can be a serious side effect of Dextroamphetamine.

One highly promoted brand of Dextroamphetamine sells for 20 times the cost of others with the identical formula, so talk to your doctor and pharmacist about price before you buy.

Again, caution: This drug is not recommended by the authors. It is given here only because it is sometimes prescribed by doctors. If so, there are ways to save money.

4. Diethylstilbestrol, U.S.P.

A synthetic that duplicates the estrogenic effects of natural female. hormones. (A natural extract from the urine of horses is 25 times as expensive as the most often prescribed "hormone" described here, yet no superiority has ever been proved. Talk to your doctor if he prescribes anything other than diethylstilbestrol for menopausal problems.)

5. Digitalis, U.S.P.

Far older than aspirin and just as respected, Digitalis acts by increasing the force and efficiency of the action of the heart muscle.

The drug comes in tablet, pill and capsule form, all equally effective but, here again, some brands cost as much as 10 times more than others. Insist, again, that your prescription be for the generic drug; then, make your choice.

6. Diphenhydramine Hydrochloride, U.S.P.
This antihistamine is an inexpensive antinauseant, and is also effective against motion sickness. Dimenhydrinate (Dramamine) is sold as a specific for anti-motion sickness but is far more expensive than the first named drug which is also effective. For mild nausea, inexpensive pheno-barbital is effective.

Price to your druggist is three times as high for some brands as for others. Urge your doctor not to specify one of the expensive ones.

7. Ephedrine Sulfate, U.S.P.
This particular bronchodilator is for asthma sufferers.

Costs more than Aminophylline, U.S.P., which is also effective, but the effect of the first is longerlasting. Careful shopping with a prescription calling for the U.S.P., not the brand name, can save close to $10 on one bottle.

8. Ferrous Sulfate, U.S.P.—prescribed for iron deficiency
The addition of supplements in tablets prescribed for iron deficiency sends the price up. Anyway, ferrous sulphate should be given "as is" for anemia. The price to your druggist for 1,000 tablets may be only a few dollars or more than 6 or 7 times that much depending on the brand name and the "coating" which has no effect on the action of the tablet.

9. Hydrocortisone Ointment, U.S.P.
This washable skin cream containing steroid is prescribed by many doctors for skin disorders.

A few years ago, according to Richard Burack, M.D., author of "The Handbook of Prescription Drugs," the least costly way to obtain a substantial amount of a washable cream containing steroid was to have the pharmacist make it up. (His suggested recipe for 3 ounces of cream: Three ounces of petrolatum, 1 gram of hydrocortisone powder. Anticipated cost, about $3.50.) Our pharmacist reports that in his opinion it is less expensive to buy steroid cream already made up from a generic source in one of 4 or 5 standard strengths and sizes. Check prices here before you buy.

10. Insulin Injection, U.S.P.—for diabetes
Less convenient but no more expensive than oral blood-sugar-lowering agents. There is not much difference in price of brands for 10 cc of insulin, which is expensive because it must be extracted from animal tissue.

11. Nitroglycerin, U.S.P.
When dissolved under the tongue, nitroglycerin relieves pain in chest called angina pectoris. Some tablets, with identical formula, cost your pharmacist twice as much as others. You're the one who pays.

12. Paregoric, U.S.P.
An antidiarrheal agent.
Far less expensive and even more effective than new brand name products prescribed for the same cause.

13. Phenobarbital, U.S.P.
When given in small doses this is the "tranquilizer" most often given to anxious patients for their soothing effect and to relax taut muscles. When given in a larger dose, the drug serves as a sleeping pill.

   Both the 15 milligram tablet (sedative or tranquilizer dose) and the 100 milligram tablet (sleeping pill) are less expensive than the highly promoted brand name tranquilizers and sleeping pills which give much the same effect.

   Get "tranquilizers" for the lowest possible price; your druggist pays about a dollar for *a thousand tablets*. You certainly should pay no more than $2 for 50. Even then, you are paying 40 times what he paid.

14. Phenylephrine Hydrochloride, U.S.P.—Nose Drops
Purpose: to relieve nasal congestion. Sold over the counter by the ounce, but not recommended by either doctors or pharmacists for everyday use because of possible serious side effects. (Blood pressure sometimes goes up; heart action becomes irregular.)

   Insist when buying this drug on getting the lowest priced drops in this generic category. Cost to the manufacturer for

all ingredients in a gallon of solution is less than $6; some
drops (example, Neo-Synephrine) are sold by druggists for
somewhere in the neighborhood of $1.25 an ounce. This
means that a gallon of material with ingredients adding up
to less than $6 is eventually sold to the over-the-counter
buyer for more than $160.

15. Potassium Penicillin G Tablets, U.S.P. (Buffered)
Prescribed for many years for streptococcal infections of
the throat and tonsils, which can lead to rheumatic fever;
to combat staphylococcus; to get rid of infections like
impetigo, etc.

    Should be reasonable (costs your druggist less than $3
for 100 tablets) so figure accordingly and insist on a
low-priced brand. Penicillin is penicillin, and every batch to
be sold in the United States must be "certified" by the
Food and Drug Administration of the United States
government.[6]

Also available: Potassium Penicillin G Tablets, U.S.P.,
(Soluble)

A convenience product to be dropped in milk or fruit juice
for children and adults who find pill-swallowing difficult.
Price should be no more than for regular penicillin. If
more, ask for a lower-priced brand.

16. Prednisone, U.S.P.
Has the same adrenal cortex steroid action as cortisone
which relieves the arthritic pain, but causes less salt and
water retention.

    More than 80 companies market Prednisolone, U.S.P.,
similar to Prednisone. The two generic drugs can be used
interchangeably, are marketed in a wide price range.

17. Progestogen, plus Estrogen in pill form—as an oral contraceptive
An oral contraceptive pill, which is not as yet considered a
basic drug but which does prevent pregnancy. Prices of the
drug made by many companies are in the same range. Here,
because there is no U.S.P. formula, the patient may as well
follow her doctor's and/or pharmacist's prescription, even
as to brand name. Later, when more is known about the
pill and its effect, a new look can be taken.

18. Reserpine, U.S.P.
    A drug that lowers blood pressure.
    Manufactured only by S. B. Penick & Company, New York, but marketed by a number of drug companies at wholesale prices ranging from less than $1.50 per thousand to more than $25.

19. Sulfisoxazole, U.S.P.
    An antibacterial drug used to combat infection in the urinary tract.
    High-priced brands cost about twice as much as some less advertised brands *with exactly the same formula.*

20. Tetracycline Hydrochloride, U.S.P.
    Often called the "work horse of antibiotics." Check prices here, because you can pay $3 more for 100 capsules for one brand over another with the same formula. (Chlortetracycline Hydrochloride, N.F., is marketed under one brand name only, Aurcomycin. Oxytetracycline, N.F., has been marketed under one trade name, Terramycin, but the patent has recently expired. It is now available in several generics and the price to you should come down.)

21. Thiazides
    A diuretic which helps in high blood pressure and heart disease.
    Available now only by brand name; least expensive is Lakeside Laboratory's Metahydrin.

Before going to a doctor with a specific complaint (i.e., angina pectoris pain), read down the list of 21 most prescribed drugs and select the one you believe he will prescribe. If he does so, make sure that he does not specify one particular brand. If he suggests a new drug, ask him why. Learn more about drugs and you will pay less.

When all is said and done, *your physician must do the prescribing.*

This chapter was not written to encourage you to prescribe special drugs for yourself, or to tamper with the considered recommendations or dosage decisions of a reliable doctor. The actual writing of a prescription has to be up to the physician. You can, however, be a well-informed consumer. The information given here is designed to help you (and your doctor) see ways to save money when buying drugs which are restricted by the Food and Drug Administration to "prescription sales only."

---

[1] A shrewd fellow near us asks his doctor to prescribe no more than a five-day supply of a given drug from our local discount druggist. At the same time, he orders a larger supply from the Blank Drug Corporation, 1550 Fifth Avenue, Bay Shore, N. Y., 11706. Send there or to other mail order companies for quotations—then, send along your doctor's prescription and place your full order there, if the prices are low, which is likely.

[2] Since the publication in 1967 of the new "Handbook of Prescription Drugs," by Richard Burack, M.D., more and more thoughtful laymen are encouraging the ordering of prescription drugs by their generic rather than their brand names as a money-saving principle. Here is a quote from a recent column by Gene Brown, syndicated in the Danbury News Times:

"Do you use Librium, Orinase, Diuril, Indocin, Lanoxin, Doriden, etc.? If you do, New York Magazine reviews the new Handbook of Prescription Drugs by Richard Burack, M.D., and says that you can save considerably by having your physician prescribe them under their generic names if he is convinced of equal efficacy.

"The generic names are in parenthesis: Orinase (tolbutamide), Librium (chlordiazepoxide hydrochloride), Diuril (chlorothiazide), Indocin (indomethacin) (aspirin is cheaper and safer), Lanoxin (digoxin), Doriden (gultehimide). (The book claims there are far less expensive substitutes.)

"Phenobarbital is marketed under its generic name and according to the article it is the least expensive and best of the popular sedatives.

"Please remember that in all the above cases, your physician, knowing your system, elementary and alimentary, may insist on a certain brand for good and sufficient reason. Follow his or her advice."

[3] This list of drugs does not constitute a recommendation—it is given here as a price-saving guide for your quick reference when your doctor writes out a prescription.

[4] Buy and save on vitamins and other pharmacy products through an organization like the American Association of Retired Persons, of which you may be a member. Price-saving example: Geritol tablets at our local discount store, 100 for $4.75; through the AARP catalogue, 100 for $4.50 delivered. AARP's comparable tonic tablets, containing B complex, Vitamin C, Brewer's yeast and iron, 100 for $2.75. Write to AARP above located at 1224 24th Street, N. W., Washington, D. C., 20037, for details.) Prices here are given for comparison only; naturally, they may change.

[5] This is definitely not a recommendation; the drug is listed here only because it is prescribed by some doctors during a weight reduction regime.

[6] Recently, the usage of Potassium Penicillin G Tablets has been decreasing. Two drugs that are becoming more and more popular now are Penicillin V and Ampicillin.

3

A Five-Step Formula for Cutting the Cost of Every Pill or Prescription You Buy

After reading the first two chapters in this book, you can write your own money-saving formula for buying pills and prescriptions. Here is the foolproof recipe.

1. Know exactly what each pill or prescription you ask for is supposed to do for you.
2. Know the ingredients in every pill or prescription you pay for and don't pay for combinations of drugs obviously concocted for promotion reasons.
3. When a specific drug is called for, ask for it by its *generic*, not its brand, name.[1]
4. Patronize a store which you know from experience sells drugs at a discount.
5. Insist on a straight talk from your doctor and pharmacist, or *switch*.

This simple formula is one that any doctor will approve in the abstract. However, in an actual doctor-patient relationship, discus-

45

sion about the cost of drugs may be uncomfortable for both participants. It will be up to you to erase this discomfort, and that takes some doing.

If you want to save money on prescription drugs, you are obviously going to have to talk to your doctor about what and where you will buy. Still you can't seem to question your doctor's judgment. This calls for diplomacy.

A TIME FOR TACT

Contrary to the belief of some consumers, few doctors and pharmacists are "in cahoots" to make you spend more for drugs. You don't have to worry that your doctor is getting a kickback from the local drug store. However, unless you tell him otherwise, your doctor may call your prescription into a local pharmacy which is not a discount store where you know drugs cost far less. The average doctor will oblige if you ask him in advance to call the discount store you have in mind. (Or better yet, ask him to write his prescription so that it can be filled in *any* drug store.) Getting the doctor to write down the generic name instead of a brand name, however, may not be quite so easy. By the time he is ready to write down a *specific* drug, he's sold.

Few patients realize that doctors are subject to the same advertising techniques as a consumer. Medical journals are filled with ads by drug companies for new wonder drugs; salesmen from these firms call on him with samples and specific directions for using these drugs; he receives convincing clinical reports. Also, your doctor sees the same commercials and reads the same magazines you read. So he's sold two ways. Or three ways, really, because his patients also exert pressure.

Talk to any doctor, and he'll tell you that about one out of three patients who report symptoms call for a specific prescription for hormones, penicillin, a vitamin B shot, cortisone or some other product after an article on it has appeared in *McCall's, Cosmopolitan, Reader's Digest* or some other popular magazine. By the time dozens of patients have called for a given drug and many ads and drug salesmen have made their pitch, your doctor may have seen good results from a given drug and is convinced that what he is suggesting will bring relief, as it well may. Questioning his decision at this point can imply a lack of trust in his judgment, and this you want to avoid. The best way to do this is to talk only in terms of cost, which implies a money-saving need on your part, not a lack of wisdom in him.

IT WILL PAY YOU TO
ASK FOR THE GENERIC DRUG

The time to talk with your doctor about specifying a drug by its generic name is when you ask him to call the drug store you want to go to. You can simply say that this is another way for you to save money. *Do not question his judgment in prescribing the generic drug he is prescribing; that's why you are in his office. But do talk about the high cost of drugs and how you are trying to cut down in every way.*

If he has prescribed a drug, as doctors used to prescribe placebos (sugar pills) simply because he thinks you expect him to do *something,* your request will encourage him to think deeper into your problem and its solution.

A woman we know recently stopped in at her doctor's office to ask him to prescribe a sleeping pill for a distraught friend in her home who had recently been divorced. As the doctor started to write down "Nembutal," she asked him to prescribe the drug under its generic name (sodium pentobarbital, U.S.P.) which could make for a cut of 75 percent in the cost of the prescription. As he thought this through, the doctor asked that the friend be brought to the office, discovered that she had an over-acting thyroid and worked out a long-range therapy.

Even in the wealthy sections of large cities where the number of doctors per 1,000 patients is higher than the national average of just one for every 1,750 Americans, dedicated specialists are forced to cram too many conferences about and with patients into too few hours, and *family doctors are really pushed.*[2] With this kind of pressure, it is understandable that the name of a well-promoted drug for an obvious symptom comes automatically to a doctor's mind in a time of need just as a well-promoted food product comes to a busy housewife's mind when she is making a decision about dinner.

The more you can help your doctor to understand in a matter of minutes why you have come to him, the better able he will be to deal with any problem you are describing. And the franker you decide to be about wanting to save money, the lower the cost is bound to be for whatever he wants you to take.

LEARN TO SEE THROUGH
TV COMMERCIALS AND PUBLICITY "PLANTS"

Unless you have a chronic physical disability (and sometimes even then), the total cost of pharmaceuticals at your house at the end of the year is conditioned pretty much by your susceptibility to drug advertising and publicity. You can correct this. Here's the way.

Right now, write down what physical problem bothers you more than any other. Maybe, you will write down "headache" or "stomach-ache" or "too many colds." Or you may say "hay fever" or "arthritis" or "gas pains" or something else. For one week, beginning now, make a note of every product you see advertised in a television commercial for your particular problem, every remedy you read about in a magazine article, every ad you see in print. When you have your list of products, all promising relief, go to a discount drug store, and *forgetting all advertised claims,* read the list of ingredients on every box or bottle on your list. Chances are the same generic drug (aspirin for headaches, for instance) will be the basic ingredient in all of the products on your list. Anything else in the product is there *mainly for a promotion reason.* Soon, you will be able to see *into* the advertising and discover what it is that the manufacturer is promoting that sets this product apart from the others. When you get to this point, you will either take the generic drug needed to do what you want it to do "as is," or you will mix your own prescription in or out of your stomach.

NATURE'S BEST BLENDER

As you begin to react to ingredients rather than claims, you will find yourself mixing ingredients *in your stomach,* which is the best blender of all. Suppose, for instance, you read on a bottle of Anacin that it contains caffeine and aspirin. (Good sense, because caffeine helps headache in a different way from aspirin.) Next time, drink a cup of strong black coffee after taking aspirin; you will get the same effect. Or, when you see sodium bicarbonate along with aspirin, listed as an ingredient in a buffered headache remedy, you can wash down an aspirin tablet with a little soda in water. Get rid of the physical problem you have as efficiently as possible; but don't pay for a little plus of this and that. *Shop for basics, and you will save money as surely as you do when buying groceries.* And when you see that an extra ingredient or two makes good sense, do your own mixing *internally*. No doctor will object.

HOW TO BE PREPARED
FOR SIMPLE EMERGENCIES

When you have a headache, you want relief now. So, if you are driving when the throbbing starts, you are going to rush into nearest store and pay whatever is asked. And, if your child has a sudden stomach-ache and you become over anxious, you may have to go to the expense of an unnecessary doctor visit. And if your arthritic mother tells you to pick up an expensive remedy which promises quick relief, who are you to refuse? An emergency is no time for fussing around, so *be prepared.*

Here's a five-way plan:

1. Carry a pill box with aspirin and whatever other pills you may need.
2. Keep a kit of simple emergency supplies in your bag or car when traveling.
3. Make sure that your regular doctor has a viewpoint similar to yours. (If he refuses to prescribe drugs by their generic name and/or gives you "manufacturer's talk" which you have heard in TV commercials, and resents any discussion of price and insists on sending you to your town's most expensive pharmacy, look for another doctor whose attitude is more compatible with yours.) This does not mean you are going to approach your doctor with skepticism. You are simply going to be realistic. There is no doubt about it. Without your doctor's cooperation, you are going to spend more.
4. Shop around for a pharmacist who is on your side. (If he charges more than other pharmacists for the same product, plays a "mystery game" about ingredients, asks you to come back in 40 minutes for pills you know he's dipping out of a barrel, switch to a man who talks straight. This does not mean that you will push to get more for less; the pharmacist is in business to make a profit, too. But it does mean that you will expect to be treated as an adult.) Your pharmacist's attitude, like your doctor's, is all important when you're aiming to beat the high cost of medicine.
5. When the chips are down, do what your doctor says. (Follow instructions exactly when emergency strikes. Your doctor is

the trained professional, not you. Let him fight your battle with pharmacists and the hospital; you relax. This will speed your recovery.) Here is where a well-established relationship pays off.

To save you money is the basic purpose of this book. It accomplishes this by bringing you information not always available to consumers. Being a knowledgeable consumer will help you two ways. (1) You cannot be oversold in the market place; (2) when serious illness strikes, you will appreciate why it is important to cooperate with your doctor. This cooperation works to hasten recovery, which frees your doctor to go on to more serious cases and cuts back on your medical costs. There is no better way to beat the high cost of medical care than to be well informed.

---

[1]Sometimes the brand name is the same as the generic name. The reason: when a new drug is approved by government and medical agencies, it is given a generic name, but for 17 years after its introduction, neither the drug nor the process can be duplicated by another manufacturer. During these years, the brand and generic name may be the same. Afterward, when the patent runs out, the original maker continues to use the brand name, but any other company can produce the drug under its generic name. Often, when this happens, the brand and generic name are entrenched *as one* in the consumer's mind, so the average man continues to buy the "name brand" rather than the identical but less expensive product made by another maker.

[2]In 1970, the president of the American Academy of General Practice, Dr. Edward J. Kowalewski, reported to a Senate health subcommittee that there was *only one family doctor for every 3,171 persons in this country.* He made the point that the number of Americans depending on one general practitioner had tripled in forty years.

PART TWO

Descriptions of More Than 200 Everyday Illnesses and Injuries and What to do For Each One

4

When Your Baby is New: How to Avoid Big Spending Without Being Neglectful

The average baby leaves the hospital as healthy as a young animal. His eyes have been treated with silver nitrate drops to prevent blindness. Any internal or external defect has been noted and pointed out. He is gaining on mother's milk or a new formula has been prescribed. New foods and vitamins have been suggested for the future.

Barring accident or serious illness, the average baby will end up his first year with an alert mind and a tripled birth weight. Mothers know this, but still they worry and go to a doctor unnecessarily. For such mothers, here is a five-step money-saving plan.

FIVE WAYS TO SAVE MONEY DURING THE BABY'S FIRST YEAR

1. Once a month during his first six months take your new baby to a doctor or clinic for a checkup and shots.[1] Between six months and one year, go two more times. After each of

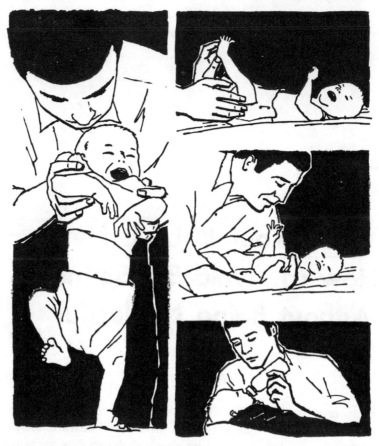

Figure 4-1: New Babies Are Stronger Than You Think: Your baby of 3 weeks or more has normal reflexes if he reacts to a given stimulus.

(Left) Inborn Stepping Reflex: Hold your baby erect with feet lightly touching a surface, and his feet will move as if walking. This is the inborn stepping reflex. **(Upper Right)** The Babinski Sign: Touch the sole of his foot and his toes will curl up. This is the Babinski sign. After 12 or 13 months old, the toes will curl down. **(Middle Right)** Grasp Reflex: Hold out your finger and feel the mighty clutch of your baby's fingers. This grasp reflex, which is present at birth, gradually disappears by 3 months. **(Lower Right)** Rooting Instinct: Touch your baby's cheek with a bottle nipple and he will turn toward it with an automatic sucking action. This is the rooting instinct which helps him to get the nipple in his mouth and suck.

these eight sessions, do what the doctor says and pay no attention to others. Switching foods and methods can be upsetting to the baby and costly.

2. Do not call the doctor between checkups unless your baby is injured or seriously ill. Only if he vomits persistently, has severe diarrhea, coughs with a racking cough, refuses to eat for three feedings or more, screams with pain or is unusually drowsy, should you call for advice. Otherwise, talk to your doctor only at the time reserved for you.

3. Between checkups, write down any questions you may have for your doctor about minor eating, sleeping and behavior problems. This will save time in the examining office and help you to correct problems that could be costly if allowed to get worse.

4. If you are eligible, go to a Well Baby Conference or Clinic[2] rather than to a private pediatrician. Or take your baby to the Baby Clinic in a nearby medical school or to the Outpatient Department where fees are figured on a sliding scale according to "ability to pay."[3] If you are not eligible for reduced medical care, do some sleuthing among your friends for a doctor who will provide your baby's first year care for a reasonable fee. Never pay extra for a "social" or "in" pediatrician.

5. With the help of this book, learn to take care of day-to-day emergencies, like the ones listed on page 49, with the skill of a professional.

QUICK RELIEF FOR 15 TYPES OF UPSETS

1. Bites (chigger and mosquito)

Chiggers (also called harvest mites and redbugs) cause itching, redness, swelling. To relieve, apply phenolated camphor solution in pure mineral oil. To prevent infestation, dust baby's pants and socks *one time only* with DDT.

Mosquito bites can become infected if scratched. Cut baby's fingernails. To relieve itching, apply cool paste of soda and water to bite or give baby oatmeal bath. Never spray repellent on baby's skin or near bed. Instead, cover bassinet with netting.

2. Colds, Coughs, Croup and/or Stuffy Nose

Mother's milk gives an immunity from colds for first three months. Afterward, cold can come from exposure by older child.

To relieve, give more water than usual, go light on solid foods, keep baby quiet in room, and don't handle. Never give "cold medicines," and report symptoms to a doctor by telephone if temperature goes above 102° with rectal thermometer. Oncoming whooping cough, measles or an allergy can produce cold-like reactions.

Coughing is unusual in a baby, is a true sign of illness. Usually means croup, virus, allergy or mucous dripping down back of nose. Treat as for croup.

Croup comes when cold settles in larynx and causes swelling of vocal cords so that baby has difficulty in breathing. This frightens baby and aggravates croup. To relieve, keep child in warm room with vaporizer or hold frightened child in arms in bathroom (where you have produced steam with hot shower) until wheezing stops.

When mucous from cold stops up nose, put a few drops of lightly salted sterile water (1/4 tsp. salt to pint of water) in nose; suck out loose mucous with small syringe which should have a rubber bulb, plastic tip and cost no more than $1.25.* Sterilize syringe in boiling water after each use.

3. Colic

Air bubble or over-eating may cause stomach distress, which along with excitability may cause colic. To relieve distress, which is marked by baby's crying, pulling up legs and expelling gas, pat baby's stomach and lay him on stomach so gas can be expelled. Give small feedings for awhile; do not overstimulate. If condition persists, mention to doctor at checkup time. He may recommend antispasmodic.

4. Constipation

When a formula does not provide enough bulk, stool may become hard enough to tear rectum and produce blood. To relieve, use brown rather than granulated sugar in formula. Give tsp. prune juice, but no more than tsp. once a day with formula. Add more fruits to diet.

5. Crossed Eyes or Strabismus, where eyes may cross or turn out

No need to report this to doctor until checkup time. Up to four months, eyes do not focus correctly; crossed eyes are common.

6. Fever

A cold or infection can raise baby's temperature, which mother can *feel.* At such time, take temperature with rectal thermometer, which will run about 1 degree higher than when taken by mouth. If temperature reading is above 102° and stays up for more than an hour, look for other symptoms and report as with cold. With any fever, give extra amounts of water to prevent dehydration due to loss of perspiration.

7. Hiccups

This involuntary spasm of the diaphragm is common, can be relieved with a drink of water and a burp over mother's shoulder.

8. Jaundice

An immature liver at birth allows a small amount of bile to accumulate in blood stream which gives yellowish tinge to skin and whites of eyes, especially in "preemies." The yellow color will disappear.

9. Scratches or Minor Cuts

To prevent scratches, line bassinet with soft material, keep sharp objects out of reach of creeping baby. To treat cut, encourage bleeding which cleanses cut, and wash wound with soap and water. Press wound to stop bleeding. If blood gushes, wound may need stitches (see page 93).

For puncture wound, soak hand or foot in hot water containing epsom salt to encourage bleeding. Then, take child to hospital for tetanus booster.

10. Skin Problems (Chafed, chapped or dry skin, diaper rash, prickly heat, winter itch, ringworm of the scalp)

For chafed skin, caused by rubbing together thighs which are wet with urine, add 1/2 tsp. of soda to baby's bath, dry bottom thoroughly. Expose skin as often as possible to air.

For chapped skin, which comes from cold dry air blowing against skin, apply vaseline and keep baby indoors if weather is windy and cold.

For dry skin, which may peel (common in new babies), clean with baby lotion or hand lotion rather than soap and water for a few days.

For diaper rash, caused by ammonia in urine or acid bowel movements, change frequently and expose clean, dry skin to air as often as possible. (Remember, there is no diaper rash without a diaper.) Apply vaseline at bedtime to keep acid from touching skin.

For impetigo characterized by red raised crusting sores, wash with an antibacterial soap twice a day and scrub off crusts. Cut nails. Put Bacitracin Neomycin on sores and in nostrils and under fingernails. Isolate child's towels. Keep skin exposed to sun.

For prickly heat, caused by perspiration which becomes trapped in pores to cause red pimple-type spots and blisters, take off some of baby's covers, and dress him in cotton, not wool. Keep skin cool, clean and dry. Give occasional soda water bath.

For ringworm of the scalp, a contagious fungus infection that can cause hair to fall out leaving bald rings, clip hair and keep scalp, combs, brushes immaculately clean. Apply Whitfield's Ointment, U.S.P. Or give Griseofulvin, U.S.P., orally. For this, get doctor's prescription.

For chafe-type winter itch, cleanse skin with mineral oil instead of soap and water. After bath, put Petrolatum, U.S.P., on wet skin to hold in moisture. Keep plants well watered to humidify room.

11. Spitting Up

If baby spits up after meals, put him on his right side in crib with head elevated on a folded diaper or two. If your baby vomits with force, the cause is more serious. (See Vomiting, page 84.)

12. Stuck Eyelids

Wash with warm lightly salted water. If eyelids remain inflamed, local infection may be present which requires drops or ointment which your doctor can prescribe by phone.

13. Accidental swallowing of smooth object

Don't panic if your baby swallows a button, pebble or even a peach stone. Once swallowed, even large objects, if fairly smooth, will pass through the baby's intestine without strain.

14. Teething

At about 7 months, baby's upper front teeth erupt; others come in soon with sore gums and a low-grade fever and digestive disturbances. Sympathize with baby. Give him rubber ring to chew on. Older baby (one year or more) can have 3/4 baby aspirin or 1/5 of a regular aspirin 2 times a day.

15. Weaning problems

If baby is weaned too abruptly, he will feel deprived. Begin gradually at five or six months by presenting a cup for one or two meals a day. Allow baby to have bottle at night for several months.

Except in rare cases, none of the above problems is a cause for alarm. Conditions described in the next chapter may be more serious.

----

*Look for products like this for as little as 10 or 20 cents at church rummage sales. Careful sterilizing insures safety.

[1]At the end of the first year, your baby will have had a series of diptheria, tetanus and whooping cough shots, a smallpox vaccination and polio immunization and a Tine test for TB.

[2]You do not have to be a welfare client to be eligible for free or reduced cost for medical care for your baby or preschool child. Many family services agencies, supported by private, government or Community Chest funds, make their Well Baby Clinics available to mothers who are trying to take the best possible care of their children at minimum cost. To find whether your town has such a clinic, call your local Welfare Office (listed under State Offices) or Visiting Nurse Association. Then call the clinic and talk to a nurse or the volunteer on duty. If you have a large family or have had unusually large medical expenses, you will be given permission to take your baby to the clinic even though your family income would be considered adequate under normal circumstances.

[3]Sometimes for such clinics, you need a reference from your family doctor or local Welfare Department.

5

What to do For a Child
When Trouble Comes Suddenly

Few children grow up without suffering from a wound or sudden attack that worries and/or mystifies their parents. This chapter helps you to deal intelligently with such emergencies.

WHEN A CUT IS DEEP

Figure 5-1 shows how to know whether a wound needs stitches . . . and, if so, what to do.

HOW TO BE A DETECTIVE
WHEN YOUR BABY IS SERIOUSLY ILL

When a child suddenly loses consciousness. . . .

- Did he fall? (Examine head for lump.)
- Has he fainted? (Is he in closet? Had a nosebleed?)
- Is he choking? (Check mouth and throat.)
- Are lungs filled with water? (Is baby in the bathtub?)
- Poisoned? (Is there an open bottle of aspirin nearby?)
- Bitten by poisonous insect? (Is there evidence of a bite?)
- Has he had an electric shock? (Near a frayed cord?)
- Exhausted from the heat? (Has he been playing in the hot sun?)

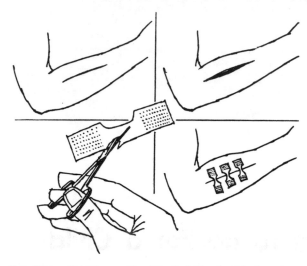

Figure 5-1: How To Know if a Wound Needs Stitches . . . and, if So, What to Do:
(Upper left) The wound on this arm does not need stitches. Note how the edges of the wound come together. The skin will mend on its own. (Upper right) The wound on this arm needs stitches. Note how the wound gapes. The skin will not mend on its own. When a wound is deep, you can aid healing with homemade butterfly bandages. Cut each one as shown here. Pull edges of the wound together and apply bandages crosswise over slit. Often, a deep, clean cut will heal without stitches when bandaged this way.

- Asphyxiated? (Is there toxic gas in the room?)

When a child is crying with a high, sharp, screaming sound. . . .

- Abdominal trouble? (Fists clenched and his legs drawn up?)
- Blood in urine or stool? (Has he vomited a whole meal?)
- Earache? (Is he rubbing ear? Is there drainage?)

If the cry is a low moan. . . .

- Does the baby have diarrhea?
- A nervous hacking cough?
- A fever?
- A rash?
- Is child vomiting?

When the child is having a convulsion, signified by eyes that roll up, stiff or shaking body, change in consciousness. . . .

- Skin hot? (This can mean infection or meningitis.)
- Cool? (This could mean epilepsy.)

WHAT TO DO WHEN YOU DECIDE WHAT'S WRONG

In case of a fainting spell, lay child flat and cover with light blanket. Child will come to almost immediately.

For a head blow, lay child flat and turn head to permit drooling. See Figure 5-2. Dial 0 for ambulance.

Figure 5-2: Head Wound. To stanch flow of blood, apply pressure with clean cloth directly on wound.

Poisoned? Arouse child, if possible. Encourage vomiting unless poison is one like kerosene (see page 77). Give water. Head for hospital, taking poison container along.

For electric shock, drowning, asphyxiation, give mouth-to-mouth resuscitation (see page 94).

To remove foreign object from air or food passage, turn baby or child upside down and smack between shoulder blades. See Figure 5-3.

Figure 5-3: Procedure to help dislodge foreign objects from air or food passage.

BROKEN BONE

To determine whether there's a fracture,[1] take note of swelling, pain to the touch, splintered skin, a twist or other deformity. Try to piece together what happened.

What to do: Keep broken place and nearby joints (which can pull muscles and disturb broken pieces) as quiet as possible. If arm is broken, child may walk, if necessary, but if leg is broken, wait for help. Put leg on pillow and encourage stillness.

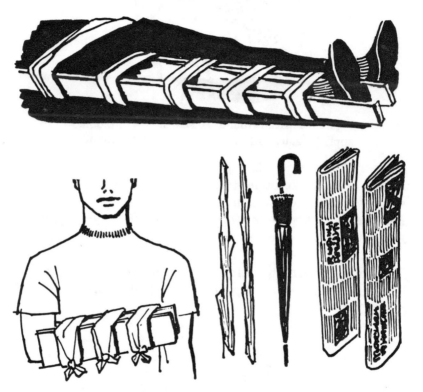

Figure 5-4: Various elements used in making emergency splints. (Courtesy of Boy Scout Handbook, 7th Edition, 6th Printing.)

To prevent a sharp broken bone from moving and tearing the flesh, keep the broken limb immovable with splints, which should be longer than the bone which they are protecting and well padded. When regulation splints are not available, sticks, umbrellas

· or folded newspapers can be used. Clothing, crumpled paper or pillows can be tied on for padding.[2]

-----

[1]There are three types of fractures: (1) simple fracture where the skin is not broken; (2) compound fracture where the skin has been pierced by a broken bone that has slipped through the skin and returned; (3) comminuted fracture where bone is shattered and skin may be opened or closed.

[2]Suggestion, courtesy of Boy Scout Handbook, Seventh Edition, 6th Printing.

6

How to Cope with 40 Childhood Problems that are Bound to Cause Worry

Some problems of children will clear up by themselves. Others need immediate attention. Knowing which are which can save your nerves and your pocketbook.

Below are descriptions of 40 childhood disturbances. When faced with a problem, look under the proper heading for what to do.

1. BIRTHMARK OR CYST

"Strawberry marks" or purple patches on face of neck will usually fade without treatment. Dark brown moles which may be hairy need no attention unless they increase in size. Then, a doctor can remove in his office where he will make skin cancer tests. Most moles are benign.

Sebaceous cysts are movable fluid-filled wens under the skin and may become large. To remove, the doctor "freezes" and cuts out in office or hospital.

2. BLOOD IN URINE, FECES OR VOMIT

Smoky-colored urine can mean scurvy, nephritis or cystitis. Blood-blackened feces can mean rectal polyp or fissure. Red vomit can mean ulcer or tumor. Before you panic, check back. Has your child eaten red beets, candy, cough drops? If blood is real, report problem now; do not wait until checkup time.

3. BRONCHOPNEUMONIA

Pneumonia in or around the bronchial tubes is caused by a virus or by bacteria such as pneumococcus. Early symptoms are a cough, chest pains, fever and chills, and occasionally blood-streaked sputum. Either type can be treated with bedrest at home, but your diagnosis should be confirmed by a doctor who will tap chest for a hollow or solid sound. (If solid, he will X-ray.)

Usual treatment is to prop child up in bed for easier breathing and give Potassium Penicillin G., U.S.P., tablets[1] (or liquid for smaller children).

If the infection has a bacterial origin, it will clear up dramatically in a day or two. Virus pneumonia requires a longer recuperation period. Child *must stay in bed until well.* Otherwise, tuberculosis, pleurisy or some other lung disorder may be aftermath.

4. CAR SICKNESS

The emotional and/or physical make-up of children causes some to become headachey, or to vomit on a long automobile trip. Such children may hate to go away from a kitten or some other loved object at home or to leave grandparents at the other end. Also, the balancing mechanism in the inner ear is more sensitive in some.

Do not overfeed a child with a history of car sickness and talk to him before you start out about where you're going and why. If he is over six, give him an inexpensive antihistamine tablet containing Diphenydramine Hydrochloride, U.S.P., which is the active ingredient in Dramamine. If he is under six, don't give antihistamine tablet but try to travel at night when he can sleep.

5. CHICKEN POX

Watery eyes, slight fever and a rash of pimples on the chest that change to blisters and scabs tell you that a child has chicken pox.

To treat, keep child in bed, giving plenty of liquids as with flu. To relieve itching, give a cool bath containing a cup or two of laundry starch. Keep child's fingernails short and hands clean to avoid infection from scratching.

6. DIARRHEA

Intestinal infection, too much brown sugar in formula or contaminated water or milk may cause diarrhea. Frequent bowel movements are loose, watery and green in color; urine may turn dark yellow which suggests child is dehydrated, a condition that is serious.

For mild diarrhea in baby, take away all food except water sweetened with white, not brown, sugar. Give older child clear broth, ginger ale and coca cola until solid food can be retained. In a dehydrated condition, breathing becomes rapid, skin is dry, there is no moisture in mucous membranes, soft spot in skull may be sunken. These signs mean that water and minerals like sodium, potassium and chloride are being taken away in the watery stools. Sugar water or coke syrup and water given every half hour until diarrhea is corrected will be non-irritating to the intestinal tract and will keep child hydrated.

7. DIPHTHERIA

This once killed 30 percent of all infected, but is practically non-existent now due to immunization shots for babies. If you have any doubt about whether an older child is fully immunized, ask for a Schick test. If immunized, the test will be negative; if the tested area blisters or turns red, booster shots are needed.

With diphtheria, the throat becomes sore, swollen and often paralyzed. Toxic poisons may be released into the body, which can affect the heart and other organs. If the child is from another country, report a paralyzing sore throat immediately. During the first three days of diphtheria, antitoxin can be injected to neutralize the poison.

8. DOG BITE

After a dog bite, keep a close watch on both child and dog. If a dog does not have rabies, this will save your child's having a series of painfu. shots. If it does have rabies, the dog will die within two weeks ana its brain can be examined. Then, your doctor will begin a series of shots of the new duck embryo vaccine.

As for the bite itself, cleanse with soap and water to disinfect, letting water run through torn flesh. Cover with light bandage.

9. EAR PROBLEMS, INCLUDING DEAFNESS, EARACHE, MASTOID

A new baby may be deaf due to blockage of the tube going from ear to mouth. Or to a mild infection in the middle ear. Such deafness usually clears up by itself unless the mother has had German measles during pregnancy in which case there may be a nerve impairment. Rarely is a child born totally deaf, so don't panic. Just tell your doctor at checkup time.

After a severe cold, tonsillitis, flu or a childhood disease like measles, your child may have an earache which causes him to scream with pain and rub his ear. Do not put anything in an aching ear, but comfort him by holding him close to you with a soft, warmed towel over the aching ear as you wait for the prescription your doctor will have to call in.

Never neglect a middle ear infection which can lead to infection of the mastoid cells behind the ear, but *do* insist that your doctor call his prescription in to the pharmacy under its generic name. Then you can select the least expensive antibiotic of the type he suggests, which will be the same formula as that of higher priced brands.

Sometimes an odorous discharge tells you something is lodged in the ear. (The child may have poked in an eraser or bean.) Don't try to dig this out. Go to your hospital's outpatient clinic and get the resident physician to do the extracting.

To remove an insect from a child's ear, drop a little warm olive or mineral oil in the ear and let the insect float out. If the insect does not come out with the oil, go to the doctor on duty at your hospital.

10. ECZEMA

Skin becomes scaly and crusty and may exude a clear, watery lymph fluid. To relieve, keep your baby immaculately clean and avoid irritating skin with wool blanket or powders, creams or soaps. Look for an allergy cause (i.e., try taking away egg yolks for a day or two; then test other foods.) The disease is not contagious and can usually be cleared up without special medications.

11. EMOTIONAL DISTURBANCES

A child may tell you that he is unhappy due to physical or emotional reasons in his make-up or home environment through bed-wetting, headrolling, masturbation, stuttering and thumb-sucking. If you fear a deep-seated problem, you may need to talk to a psychiatrist which you can find through your local United Fund, County Medical Society, Mental Health Clinic or County Hospital or through a nearby university which may have a free clinic. For specific problems, here's what to do:

Bed-wetting: Until after the age seven, don't treat this as a problem. Afterward, reward dryness, ignore wetting and encourage your child to go longer in the daytime between urinating. For an older child who may be embarrassed, Imipramine can be of help; and in some cases, a doctor can do bladder "stretching."

Headrolling, rocking and banging: This is a form of self comfort. Read to your child at bedtime so that he feels secure as he goes to sleep.

Masturbation: This is a result of nervousness, never the cause. Like thumb-sucking, it simply tells you the child is worried about something in his life. Talk to your child about masturbating and make clear to him that this is something other children do in private. Encourage him not to masturbate in public, but do not disapprove.

Stuttering. At the first sign, listen intently to your child so that he doesn't have to over-work to get his ideas across to you. This will help ease his tension. If speech difficulty becomes more than a phase, write to a nearby college which has a speech and hearing clinic. Or write to the American Speech and Hearing Association, 9030 Old Georgetown Road, Washington D. C., 20014, for information about where to go near you.

Thumb-sucking: This habit is due to oral need, rarely effects teeth. For a thumb-sucking baby, put smaller holes in nipple of bottle. For the older child, plan things for your child to do with you with his hands.

12. EYE PROBLEMS, INCLUDING INJURIES, EYELID AND SEEING PROBLEMS

The following eye and eyelid problems can be treated at home.

Black eye is caused by bruising soft tissues around eye. Apply cold compresses to reduce swelling and stop under-the-skin bleeding. Tape light dressing over eye until soreness disappears.

Burns of the eye from strong acid or alkaline solutions: To save child's sight, wash eye immediately with cool clear water, using at least a quart. For best results, put child on side with injured eye down, holding eye open as you pour. Bandage eye lightly after washing and get to a hospital.

Eyestrain (caused by long hours of watching television): Wash eyes with saline solution (1/2 tsp. salt to one pint water). Saturate sterile cotton in water, press against eyelid at night when child goes to sleep and again in morning. Encourage him to open eyes and let salt water run in. As for TV, don't let him watch in room that is totally dark and put his chair at least eight feet from set.

Inflamed crusty eyelids: Condition can be carryover from measles or some other childhood disease or can come from dandruff or even eyestrain. Wash with same solution as for Pink Eye and encourage child to get more rest.

Pink Eye (conjunctivitis—where eyes become red and lids swell and stick together): Wash morning and night with clear water (not salt water), using clean cotton for each eye so as not to infect the other. Then, apply yellow mercury ophthalmic ointment (no prescription necessary) to lids. Apply hot compresses to eyes for five minutes so that ointment will go into eye to wash eyeball. If condition does not improve in three days' time, go to eye doctor who will give you a prescription for antibiotic.

Seeing Problems like Color Blindness and Near or Far Sightedness:

(1) Color Blindness: Child can't tell difference between green and red. More common in male than in female. No cure.
(2) Signs of Near or Far Sightedness: Child holds book too close to read. Or he squints to see things far away. Get advice and probably corrective glasses from ophthalmologist.

"Something in my eye". Pull lid down to dislodge grit. Or roll back upper lid over match stick or Q-tip, as shown here, and blot away with Kleenex as shown in Figure 6-1.

Speck still there? Wash as for Pink Eye. If the foreign object is sharp and has penetrated the cornea into the eyeball, do not try a home remedy of any kind. Cover the eye with a loose bandage, and *transport child to the hospital at once.*

Sore eyes irritated by wind, blowing sand, dust, smoke, head cold, measles, hay fever or other allergy: Relieve with salt water treatment as for eyestrain.

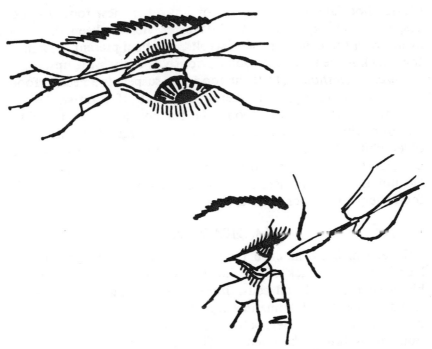

Figure 6-1: How to remove objects from the eye.

Stye: Wash with warm water and treat with yellow ointment as for Pink Eye.

Twitching Eyelids and/or Shadows under eyes: See that child gets more rest and builds up vitality.

Watery Eyes: Is cause an allergy, blocked tear duct, Pink Eye or cold? For allergy, give antihistamine; for block, ask doctor to open duct at checkup time; for Pink Eye, apply yellow ointment; for cold, work for all-over relief.

13. FOOD ALLERGY

Vomiting, dizziness, a "sick feeling" and/or hives can mean that a child is allergic to a specific food, usually a protein. (Shrimp and other shellfish, cheese, milk, nuts and pork are common offenders.) Strawberries, chocolate, wheat and other foods can also produce upsets.

If your baby is not gaining, vomits often and is listless, your doctor may suspect a milk allergy. At checkup time, he will probably recommend Sobee, Mullsoy or some other protein food instead of the usual formula. If an older child becomes ill after eating chocolate, lobster, bacon or any other new food you can suspect an allergy. Unless the attack is violent, keep this food away from the child for a few weeks, and then present it again. If the attack is the same, the food obviously is causing the upset.

Three suggestions: (1) If the food you suspect is a needed food, ask a doctor to make an allergy skin test. If positive, he will recommend a substitute food. (2) Do not make your child a neurotic with constant references to his "allergies," but do tell an older child that shrimp or some other food seems to cause an allergic reaction in him and to stay away from this for awhile. (3) Do not immediately decide that every sudden upset is due to a food allergy. Consider other causes, too.

14. HEAD LICE

Lice, which are hatched from grayish-white eggs (nits) on the hair and on the back of the head near the headline, live on the blood of the child and cause itching. Scratching can cause scabs and sore spots and, sometimes, glands can become infected. To treat, apply Benzyl Benzoate, a prescription drug, as directed.[2] Boil combs, brushes between combings and leave in alcohol.

15. HEART MURMUR

Along with the LUB DUB sound heard by a doctor when he listens to a child's chest, there may be a third murmuring sound. This tells him there may be an anatomical defect in the heart or that the child has Rheumatic fever. Often, however, it signifies nothing. Unless the doctor says there is a defect, there is nothing for a parent to be concerned about. Most heart murmurs are innocent.

16. HERNIA

An umbilical hernia (bulging naval) is common in most new babies and disappears within a few months after a baby's birth. However, a hernia in the groin, more common in boy babies than in girls, must be corrected in the hospital to prevent a strangulated hernia later on. Strangulation takes place when a loop of bowel comes through the surrounding tissue and becomes stuck, causing extreme pain and, sometimes, death. *Never neglect a hernia.* Once corrected, forget about it. There is no permanent damage.

17. INFLUENZA

This sudden lay-low disease is caused by a contagious influenza virus which changes or mutates every three years, so immunization is difficult. A child with heart trouble or a chronic disease should be given a flu shot, however, when a *known* virus is coming. A child with a high fever, headache and the extreme fatigue that comes with flu, needs bed rest, aspirin and plenty of liquids to offset the dehydration caused by prolonged fever and perspiration. Do not let a child go back to school before his usual strength returns. Flu weakens the body which makes it susceptible to other diseases.

18. MEASLES

There are two varieties. One is German Measles (or Rubella) which is a mild disease for a child but a hazard for pregnant women; the other is known as Measles, not German, (Rubeola) and is an ominous disease. Both are caused by viruses.

Rubella (German) begins with a cold, mild fever and sore throat. Within a week, a rash of flat pink spots covers the body for about two days and the glands in the neck swell. Once infected, the child has immunity for life and recovers within a few days. The big danger is that he will transfer the infection to a pregnant woman, in which case the unborn child can be affected.[3]

Rubeola (not German) begins with pink eyes that are sensitive to light, a fever, cough and puffy look. In a few days, a "measly" rash appears on the face and spreads downward. To prevent complications (ear infection, pneumonia, eye trouble and even brain damage), keep child in bed for ten days, the duration of the disease. If another is exposed, tell a doctor at once who will probably give gamma globulin to a young baby or pregnant woman.

To prevent, have your child inoculated against measles. Call your town's Communicable Disease Center, Visiting Nurse Association or school superintendent to find where free vaccine is available.[4] Your child (or you) may be spared a lifetime affliction from this peculiar disease that used to be considered harmless.

19. MENINGITIS

This serious disease, caused by several kinds of bacteria or germs, affects the meninges (three membranes covering the brain and spinal cord). Symptoms are high fever, convulsions, vomiting, stiff neck, headache, eventual lack of consciousness.

Meningitis is too serious to treat on your own, but by recognizing it in time, you can help to arrest its progress. (Penicillin, Ampicillin and Chloramphenicol are effective antibiotics in the early stage.) If you suspect meningitis, call a doctor who will probably hurry you to the "communicable diseases" section of your hospital where immediate help can be given. There is no preventive vaccine.

20. POISON IVY

Itching, redness and blisters on the skin comes as the result of contact with glossy green poison ivy shrubs or plants in the spring

Figure 6-2: Poison Ivy. Poison ivy leaves grow in clusters of three, are red in spring and fall, green and glossy in summer. Berries are white like mistletoe. Oily sap is what irritates.

or early summer when the plants are full of sap.[5] Figure 6-2 shows what this plant looks like.

Teach your child to know a poison ivy plant. Its leaves grow in clusters of three, and red in spring and fall, green and glossy in summer. Berries are white like mistletoe. Oily sap is what irritates.

If you know a child has come in contact with the plant, rinse off the oil from the plant by sudsing over and over with soap and hot water. Should the blisters appear before you know what happened, wash skin with warm water and apply calamine lotion. If a large amount of skin is involved, ask a doctor to prescribe Corticosteroid ointment by telephone and apply for from five to seven days.

21. POISONING FROM ASPIRIN, CRAYONS, PAINTS, GLUE OR ANYTHING ELSE

Your child may be abnormally drowsy and have fast breathing, and an empty aspirin bottle may tell you that he has poisoned himself. Or you may find that he has eaten moth balls, crayons or drunk drain cleaner. Your immediate objective should be to (1) get poison out of the stomach; and (2) flood stomach to slow down rate of absorption of the poison.

Except where there is danger of the vomited poison's being inhaled into the lungs (see note below), gag poisoned child with fingers or woodstick to induce vomiting. Also, give Syrup of Ipecac, U.S.P., or soda in water and/or an overdose of milk of magnesia. Force feed water amd milk, the more the better.[6]

NOTE: *For kerosene, lye and carbolic acid, don't induce vomiting. The burning that took place as the poison went down will burn again coming up. Also, the poison may be inhaled into the lungs.*

Whatever the poison, don't waste time. Start with your child to the emergency room of the hospital. Be sure to take along the container of the poison with its label and the pan of vomitus for analysis. The faster treatment begins the better.

Poisons and the Antidotes for these Poisons

If poisoned by ammonia, detergent, drain cleaner or lye, give vinegar and water (half a glass of each mixed together) followed by several glasses of plain water.

For poisoning from silver, polish, bleach, scouring powder or moth balls, give large amount of baking soda or milk of magnesia in water .

For arsenic poisoning, give egg white.

If the child swallows barbiturates, induce vomiting and give black coffee. For crayon or paint poisoning, substitute water for black coffee.

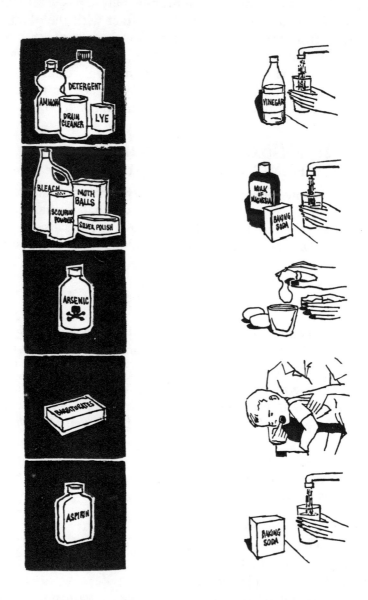

Figure 6-3: Various poisons and their antidotes.

For overdose of aspirin, induce vomiting with soda and/or milk of magnesia in water and force feed water or milk, the more the better.

22. RHEUMATIC FEVER

About two weeks after streptococcus infection a child may run a temperature, become pale, irritable and have a poor appetite. With rheumatic fever, the joints become red, swollen and painful. Often, the heart becomes affected and the child has a rapid pulse and shortness of breath. There may be a rash and (rarely) a nosebleed. The fever can result in leaking or shrunk heart valves, an injured heart covering, lining or muscle.

This disease is not as common as it was before penicillin. To prevent, take any child with a tonsil infection or severe sore throat to a clinic for a throat culture and/or start treatment with penicillin. If the infection has already resulted in rheumatic fever, you can avoid another attack with penicillin given daily.

23. ROSEOLA INFANTUM

A child under three may become fussy, sleepy and hot. In about three days, a rash of raised red marks appears, and the disease is over. No treatment is known, and one bout provides immunity for life.

24. SCARLET FEVER

This is a "strep" infection, plus toxin which causes a magenta (scarlet) colored rash. It should not be treated lightly, but it has become more mild in the last 25 years.[7] Symptoms are fatigue, restlessness which changes to fever, sore throat and vomiting. Then, a red rash covers the body but leaves the area around the mouth white-looking. The tongue becomes "strawberry colored." In two weeks the skin peels from the hands and feet.

Penicillin G "gets at" streptococcal germs and prevents ear, kidney and glandular complications.

25. SINUSITIS

Child over six[8] may constantly catch cold, which goes down into chest. Catarrh (post nasal drip) may be present. If child has a headache and a stopped up nose, give aspirin[9] at bedtime and moisten air in bedroom with a vaporizer. Phenylephrine nose drops can be helpful.

26. SMASHED FINGER

When a finger is smashed in a car door, pain is immediate and intense, whether there is a break or a bruise. To relieve, hold child's hand under cold water for as long as he wants to be there. Give appropriate aspirin dose. If blood blister forms, open with a needle (sterilized in hot flame and then cooled), wash carefully and apply band-aid. If you suspect break, make a homemade splint with an ice cream stick taped to finger to keep three finger bones quiet. Intense pain should end in a day or two.

27. SMEGNA

Sometimes, a cheeselike deposit of sebum with a disagreeable odor collects on the foreskin covering a boy's penis or in the clitoris of a girl. Skinning back the foreskin for an adequate cleaning usually prevents buildup.

28. STOMACH-ACHE

When your child has a stomach-ache, be glad if he vomits. Usually, the cramped feeling disappears, and if the cause is a food allergy, overeating or even a trace of poison (in a crayon or paints, for instance), vomiting gets rid of the problem. Do not force fluid or food right after vomiting occurs. The upset will probably subside.

Do not give a physic to a child with cramps or put a hot water bottle on his stomach. The first can cause an inflamed appendix to rupture which can lead to peritonitis and the other does no good and may burn skin.

Sometimes, a stomach-ache comes from nervousness. Search for the cause and keep your child calm and with you. If the upset is a symptom of an infection, there will be other symptoms to help you know what is the matter. Then, look in this book for what to do.

29. STREPTOCOCCUS INFECTION

This usually starts with a sore throat, which may be accompanied by a red rash, sweetish-smelling breath and upset stomach. It can lead to peritonsillar abscess, kidney infection or rheumatic fever. Make your child comfortable in bed, give liquids and aspirin. Call doctor to see if penicillin should be given.[10] If so, the drug should be given orally for ten days.

30. SUNBURN

For severe sunburn, accompanied by chills and fever, give a cooling bath to which baking soda has been added. Pat dry and apply sterile white Petrolatum, U.S.P., to burnt areas. Cover child with sheet or light blanket. Give ginger ale or water in quantities and aspirin.

To avoid sunburn, give light-skinned babies and young children gradual exposure to sun, letting them sunbathe and play outdoors in the early morning or late afternoon when rays of the sun are long and burn more slowly. Avoid letting such children stay outdoors too long on hazy days and on the beach or where sun is reflected. Cover tender skin with shirt and hat.

Figure 6-4: **Child With Shadow.** Let child play outdoors in the morning and late afternoon when rays of the sun are long.

31. SWALLOWING OF SHARP OBJECT

If a child swallows a fishbone, pin, piece of glass or anything sharp, he may pass it in his stool, so watch for it without alarming the child or even letting him know what you are looking for. Do not give a laxative, and never mind giving large amounts of bread or potatoes. Starchy foods will not "coat" offending object.

If the child swallows a large piece of broken glass, an open safety pin or a nail, go to the emergency office of your hospital for an X-ray, even if the sharp object does not stick in the child's throat. An operation may be called for.

If the child chokes, he may cough out the offending object. If not, hold him upside down and urge him to cough or induce coughing by squeezing rib cage. If open pin, fishbone or any metallic object is lodged in the throat, dial 0 and ask Operator to send ambulance. Stick fingers down throat and pull out object in any way you can if child is breathless and turns blue. If the child is dying from lack of oxygen, an emergency tracheotomy may have to be done.[11]

32. SWOLLEN GLANDS

Many healthy children have large neck glands, so only if the lymph glands are larger than usual and accompanied by a fever, should you be concerned. Then, the swelling may indicate a streptococcus infection, tonsillitis, sinusitis or even scalp infection. Or it can be a virus infection or a forerunner of tuberculosis.

The swelling is usually evidence that the child is responding normally to infection. If he has a fever, the *site* of the infection should be searched for. If the swelling is due to a streptococcus infection in the throat, Potassium Penicillin G tablets, U.S.P., will bring relief. These tablets can be dropped into a glass of ginger ale or other good-tasting soft drink or fruit juice and are most effective when the stomach is empty.

33. THRUSH

This fungus disease, characterized by whitish ulcerous spots in the mouth and throat and a bad-smelling breath, will clear up in a few days with Nystatin, U.S.P., so don't overbuy. A doctor who accepts your diagnosis can call in the name of the generic drug for you to a discount drug store where you can pick it up.

34. TONSILLITIS OR ENLARGED ADENOIDS

Tonsils are lymph glands which deflect germs and viruses which could otherwise be carried to the lungs. With the infection localized in the throat, cold symptoms appear. Also, a high temperature, swollen tonsils and, sometimes yellow spots or ulcers in the back of the throat may come. (These same symptoms may be announcing another disease, so do not jump to a conclusion, and *do not insist that tonsils come out.* Remember, they do have a function.)

The prescription usually given for a tonsil infection is Penicillin G, U.S.P., but this will have no effect if the cause is a virus, not a germ. Like a cold, virus tonsillitis usually runs the course of a week or two during which time your child should stay in bed. The biggest danger is a middle ear infection, and best procedure is bed rest, aspirin and plenty of liquids.

Adenoids are lymph glands behind the nose which, like tonsils, deflect infection. When infected or enlarged, they may interfere with breathing or block off the passage between the throat and the middle ear causing ear infection. Even so, most ear men and pediatricians do not feel adenoids or tonsils should be removed unless there is frequent middle ear infection, loss of hearing, blocked breathing, frequent abscesses, quinsy attacks and/or throat infections.

When needed, the removal of adenoids and tonsils is a simple operation.

35. TOO FAT OR TOO THIN

The fat baby over three months can have his formula thinned down and be given more fruits and vegetables and fewer servings of cereal and bananas. If he is still fat when he passes year one, he is not moving around enough, or is overeating because of loneliness or eating too many starches and sweets.[12] Get such a child interested in things outside of eating and send him at two or three to nursery school. Cut down on servings of creamy milk, bread and butter, potatoes, cookies and fried foods. Feed more proteins, fruits and vegetables.

Unless your child is losing weight from an infection, an inadequate formula or diet, diarrhea, a vitamin deficiency, a food assimilation problem or loneliness, do not worry about his being thin. Usually, this comes with an active, wiry, interested-in-everything child who is bright and healthy.

If your child is too "hyped up," encourage him to have "quiet times" during the day with you, alone. Don't be anxious about his eating; you may "turn him off" at the table. At checkup time, call the doctor's attention to a slow gain or actual loss. If he finds an infection, he can help you to correct it, and if he finds the child is not assimilating a needed food correctly, he can suggest a substitute.

36. TOOTH DECAY

When your child has his 20 first teeth, teach him how to care for them. This early habit will last for life and, anyway, when baby teeth are lost through decay, the 32 second teeth do not have enough space to come in properly.

When either a baby tooth or a first tooth is decayed, pain will occur when the child eats or drinks something hot or cold, and small black or brown spots will show on the teeth. Avoid cold and hot drinks and candy until a dentist has filled the tooth. Then, see that the child goes easy on candy and eats an orange or grapefruit instead of something sweet at bedtime. Encourage him to brush his teeth twice a day (but especially at bedtime) with fluoridated tooth paste.

To save money, avoid dental problems with good prevention methods. If trouble strikes, go, if possible, to a University Dental Clinic where undergraduate pedodontists (specialists in the care of young teeth) sometimes do work for less.

Should your child awaken in the night with a severe toothache, he may have a neuralgia-like pain (from a cold or sinusitis) associated with the same nerve. Or he may have a gumboil, which may produce swelling of the jaw. In this case, the child will have a bad taste in his mouth, and you can probably see the boil. To help your child get rest during the night, give him aspirin and a hot water bottle or heating pad on the jaw. As soon as possible, get your child to a dentist, who will lance the boil, or will repair the decayed or chipped tooth which is giving problem. To give relief while waiting for an appointment to have a tooth filled, dampen cotton with oil of cloves or just plain mineral oil and pack into the cavity (which you can locate with small mirror) with match stick. Give aspirin at bedtime.

37. VOMITING

All babies spit up, and small children may bring up a meal in a vomiting spell because of car sickness, excitement or overeating.

Vomiting with force and frequency is something quite different and can mean acute appendicitis, scarlet fever, contaminated milk, meningitis, dangerous intestinal trouble or some other problem far too serious to ignore.

Abdominal pain with vomiting can mean appendicitis; a high fever, scarlet fever; diarrhea, contaminated milk; headache, fever and convulsions, meningitis; abdominal pain and bloody mucous in stools, intussusception (which is a dangerous intestinal disorder). Look up what to do in this book if you suspect any of these problems or in the case of appendicitis, meningitis or intussesception, get to a doctor, clinic or hospital immediately.

38. WARTS

These small hard elevations, caused by a virus, are contagious and can be "caught" by one finger from another. To remove, rub two or three times a day with castor oil or apply Podophyllin. To get rid of a stubborn or disfiguring wart, a doctor may have to use an electric needle or dry ice. Never cut off a wart or try to remove a bleeding one. An oozing wart may be cancerous and should be looked at by a doctor.

39. WHOOPING COUGH

Every baby should have his first immunity shot before four months. For basic immunization, a series of three shots will be given. If a baby is exposed and through some oversight has never been immunized, he can be given a special type of gamma globulin.

Whooping cough begins with a running nose and dry cough, soon produces violent coughing and vomiting spells. The child has difficulty in breathing and pulls in his breath with a whooping sound. The disease lasts for six weeks, and because it can be fatal for babies, isolated hospital care is recommended. Older children should stay in bed with no activity that might provoke "whooping."

40. WORMS

Hookworm, more common in Southern states than in the North, gets into the body through the skin and is usually picked up from infected soil by barefoot children. The worms travel through the blood to the lungs causing coughing; then, the stomach and small intestines where the worms thrive. As the worms take protein from the body, the child becomes run down, listless and anemic. Eggs (and, sometimes, blood) appear in the stool.

Never try to deworm your child with *old wives'* medicines, many of which are so drastic, they harm the child. Tell the clinic that you have found eggs in the stool. Tetrachloroethylene, U.S.P., will get rid of them. After the child recovers, encourage him to wear sandals in a region where hookworm is a problem.

Roundworm, like hookworm, is an intestinal parasite, but is larger and is expelled in the stool. Should your child be irritable, restless and have a poor appetite, look for a roundworm in the stool and take it to the nearest clinic. Piperazine, U.S.P., is the usual prescription.

Tiny pinworms, often called "seat worms" get into the intestines in egg form through the mouth. There, they hatch into worms less than one-half inch long. At night, the female worm crawls out of the body to lay eggs in the anal region, thus causing extreme itching. The child scratches himself and reinfects himself (even as he takes "worm medicine") with eggs from under his nails.

Absolute cleanliness of bedding, the child's hands, underclothes and utensils is essential. Pyrvinium Pamoate, U.S.P., a prescription drug, can be given internally when the presence of worms is confirmed. Don't spend money for expensive rectal ointments which most doctors consider passe. Give Sitz baths only.

All children, despite the super cleanliness of the mother, can get worms, especially pinworms, and no embarrassment should be felt. With pinworms, the whole family should be treated.

DON'T BE AN OVER-ANXIOUS PARENT

Your child's welfare is important to you, but do not let yourself become neurotic on the subject. Know what to do when he is under par and where to go in an emergency, and let things go at that. He will be happier and so will you if you are not constantly hovering. Relax and enjoy these years; they flee.

---

[1]Tablets come in many brands in a wide range of prices; all have the same U.S.P. formula.

[2]Tell a doctor or the clinic by telephone that your child has head lice and ask if a prescription for Benzyl Benzoate can be called into the discount drug store nearest you.

[3]If you are pregnant and exposed to German Measles, tell a doctor at once who may suggest a legal abortion and will certainly suggest gamma globulin to help you resist the disease.

[4]Nineteen states insist on a compulsory vaccination for measles and the Department of Health in thousands of counties in other states have set up "Measles Clinics" where free vaccine is given to all children accompanied by a parent.

[5]A baby or small child may be infected without contact with the plant by a dog or cat which has crawled through ivy plants, by contact with a man's trousers or jacket or by smoke from a rubbish fire containing the plant.

[6]If the child is unconscious, keep him warm but don't try to force feed liquids. The poison has already been absorbed into the body. Get to the hospital.

[7]Many years ago, it proved fatal to Dwight Eisenhower's son.

[8]Hollows (sinuses) in cheekbones and forehead are not formed until child is from 4 to 6 years old, so sinus infection is not common in the very young. Your child may have a nasal allergy, not sinusitis, or the air in your home may be too dry, or an older child may be bringing home viruses from school. Do not be too quick to say, "Sinus trouble."

[9]Aspirin dosage; 1 grain of aspirin per year of age, 2-3 times a day

[10]He may want to swab throat and "plate" out bacteria for a throat culture. This takes 24-48 hours. If "strep" is found, he will give penicillin at once.

[11]If a foreign object blocks the air passage, the only thing you can do is cut into the hard wind pipe below the Adam's apple so that the air can come in. NEVER RESORT TO THIS EXTREME MEASURE UNLESS CHILD IS BLUE AND CLOSE TO DEATH.

[12]Fat children often come from fat parents, but no hereditary link has been established. Probably, the whole family is eating too many starches and sweets.

NO ONE SHOULD DRIVE WHO DOES NOT KNOW THESE RULES

What To Do When An Accident Happens At Night

If you come upon someone who has been run down, shot or injured in a collision . . .

1. Flag oncoming car by waving white shirt, blouse or strip of cloth.
2. Ask passerby to call 0 for police and/or ambulance. Be sure he knows exactly where you are and how near to what town.
3. If traffic is heavy, get someone to help you redirect traffic. Otherwise, put white flag on car and attend to injured person.
4. Do what you can to stop bleeding by pressing hand or cloth on wound. Otherwise keep victim quiet. Cover with coat or blanket until ambulance comes.
5. Find out where victim is being taken in ambulance.
6. If injured person is someone you know, report diabetes or any other disease he may have to ambulance personnel.
7. Get numbers of any involved cars and names of witnesses. (If you are involved, exchange license numbers, telephone numbers and the names of your insurance representatives and numbers of policies with other driver, if possible.)
8. Report what you know to the police who come . . . or call information to police, if they do not come.
9. If you are liable in any way, call your insurance man the following morning.

Should *you* be injured, do the following, if possible . . .

1. Flag oncoming car with white cloth, if possible.
2. Get someone to call ambulance and/or police.
3. Give police your AAA card, if you are a member, so that your car can be towed to a garage at no expense. (If police do not arrive before you are taken away, give someone in group your AAA number and ask him to ask garage to get your car.)
4. At hospital, give your Blue Cross and/or Major Medical Insurance policy card to admissions people. Call home before accident report comes in another way.
5. Tell the doctor on duty about any chronic condition like diabetes.
6. Next day, call your family's insurance man who handles your automobile and liability insurance. He can get facts about accident from police report.

7

How to Deal With Accidents and 31 Diseases that Occur in Adolescence

The largest increase in the death rate for both males and females, as reported in the 1970 World Almanac, occurred in the 15-24 age group. Because automobile accidents are a primary cause of the high death rate in this age bracket,[1] be sure that your child takes a driving course from a professional. Most public schools offer such courses free, and your telephone book lists other instruction places where you pay a fee.

Help your child to understand the mind distortion that comes with alcohol and/or drugs.[2] Museums, schools and police departments regularly schedule exhibits, slide shows and movies that explain the steps that lead to addiction.

Encourage children in 7th, 8th and 9th grades to take a Junior First Aid Course. Through the Red Cross, this course, like the Standard Course, for which older students are eligible, runs 10 to 12 sessions and is free. The knowledge gained here can save a life in an emergency.

On the next three pages are step by step instructions for what to do when a serious accident occurs on a ski slope, when ice skating or swimming or on the highway.

SEVEN EMERGENCIES EVERY YOUNG PERSON SHOULD KNOW HOW TO DEAL WITH

1. *A near drowning:* Someone may overestimate his strength in the water (or may fall through the thin ice) and may drown unless help comes.

   What to do: Throw out blanket or towel (or extend pole or oar or even your body), keeping hold of one end of extended towel or other lifesaver and pull swimmer to shore. See Figure 7-1 below. (Unless you are a trained life guard, this is a wiser course than to jump in to do the saving unless the person in the water is unconscious or a child.)

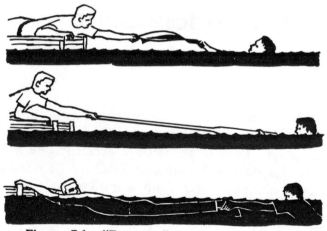

Figure 7-1: "Extension" methods to reach a drowning person.

2. *Fractured back or neck:* A friend may hit his head in an automobile crash or when diving and may lose consciousness and/or may have severe back pain.

   What to do: Because the slightest nudge of a splintered bone can cause a puncture of the spinal cord, resulting in paralysis, do not move the patient "even to make him more comfortable." Run to a telephone, and tell the operator where you are and to connect you with the nearest ambulance service. If you must move the patient, construct a frame stretcher, as directed in example three, and steady head with fingers at both sides of skull below the ears. Then, move patient "like a log," that is, keep head and neck fixed on spine. *Give no stimulant.* See Figure 7-2 below.

Figure 7-2: When back is broken, injured person should stay flat like a log.

3. *Broken leg or other fracture:* A companion spelunking on a mountain climbing, ski or hiking trip may break a bone and have to be carried back to civilization.

   What to do: Make padded splint for broken leg and transport injured person on stretched blanket if there are several in your party or on hastily constructed frame stretcher if there are two to carry. See Figure 7-3 for details.

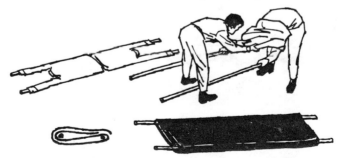

Figure 7-3: To make stretcher, put jacket and shirt on two poles or wrap blanket around poles.

   Warning: Never go caving, skiing away from the crowd or mountain climbing unless there are at least three in your party—two to carry in case one person is injured.

4. *Poisonous snake bite:* Should someone in your party be

bitten by a rattlesnake, copperhead, coral snake or moccasin, put a constriction band three inches above fang marks on arm or leg. Wash "bite" with cold water and transport patient flat to civilization. Call doctor and say you're coming for antivenom treatment.

Note: Learn to recognize a poisonous snake. Here are signs in Figure 7-4.

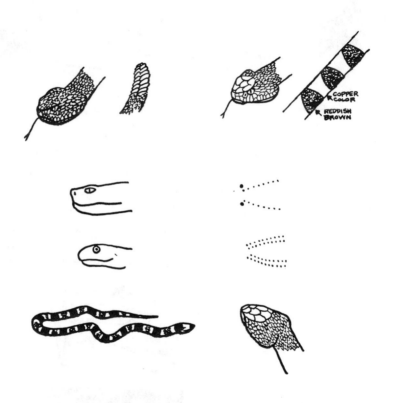

Figure 7-4: Signs of poisonous snakes.

Not every bite, even from a poisonous snake is envenomated, and reckless slashing of skin around a bite can do more harm than good in many cases. First sign that snake doing biting was poisonous: sharp local pain comes within 5 to 10 minutes. If there is no pain, there is no venom. Still, the patient should be taken to the hospital. If the hospital' is a long way off, ease stricture occasionally to let blood circulate to affected part.

5. *Spurting blood:* An accident victim on the highway or in the woods may be threatened with loss of life due to loss of blood.

   What to do: To stop severe bleeding, put pressure on bleeding point with your finger, bare hand or a pad of any cloth such as a torn piece from a shirt or shorts. This control of bleeding will give you time to get patient to the hospital which you should do as fast as possible. See Figure 7-5.

Figure 7-5: To stop severe bleeding, put pressure on bleeding point with finger, bare hand or pad of cloth.

   What about a tourniquet?: If an arm or leg is practically severed or several arteries are spurting blood that can't be stopped, make a tourniquet by tying your handkerchief between the wound and the patient's heart (an inch from the wound) and placing a stick under the twisted cloth. (This should be done only when the patient's life is ebbing away because a loss of an arm or limb can result from the tourniquet.) Get professional help as fast as possible.

6. *Poison!:* A friend may take an overdose of sleeping pills, a child may eat aspirin, a woman may be poisoned by food.

   What to do: Get rid of the poison. Remember to make attempt to get patient to vomit by use of fingers or stick. Head for professional help. In any accident, the patient will probably go into shock. Anticipate this by keeping patient's head lower than feet (unless there is a head injury, in which case keep the patient's body level.) Do not over-heat the patient with too many blankets, but do keep him from getting cold with whatever covering he needs. Stay nearby to help allay fears. Keep victim from getting cold and see Figure 7-6 for positioning instructions.

Figure 7-6: Anticipate patient's going into shock. Lower head and keep him from getting cold.

7. *Mouth-to mouth breathing:* A man may be gassed, a child may be drowning, a woman may be knocked unconscious by a bolt of electricity; what's called for then is mouth-to-nose or mouth-to-mouth breathing. Figure 7-7 shows basic technique.

Figure 7-7: For mouth to mouth breathing, breathe your own air into other person's mouth. Keep his nose or mouth closed as you breathe into his mouth or nose.

What to do: Breathe your own air into a dying person's mouth. Keep his nose closed or breathe into his nose keeping his mouth closed. In the case of a small child, breathe into both nose and mouth. Put victim face up, wipe foreign matter from mouth or nose, suck deep breath of air into your own lungs and exhale into victim's nose or mouth until you see his chest rise. Then, let air escape from victim's lungs as you take another breath and repeat. Keep filling his lungs and letting air release itself until patient is breathing under his own power.

WHEN MOUTH TO MOUTH RESPIRATION IS IMPOSSIBLE

If there is a mouth injury, use the artificial respiration method shown in Figure 7-8.[3]

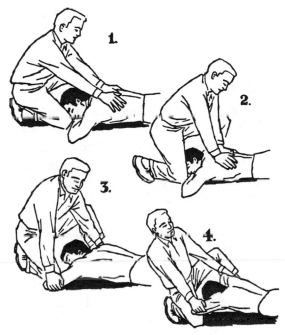

Figure 7-8: Artificial Respiration: If mouth to mouth breathing is impossible because of a mouth injury, use the artificial respiration method shown here.

1. Wipe mouth out quickly and put victim face down. Bend his elbows and place hands one upon the other, placing his head to one side with his chin jutting out.
2. Kneeling at head of victim, place hands flat on back (below armpits) and rock forward. Allow your body weight to exert steady even pressure.
3. Immediately draw arms up toward you, applying enough lift to feel tension in victim's shoulders. Lower arms to the ground.
4. Repeat the cycle about 12 times per minute. Air should flow out and in without your help within 15 minutes if there is no obstruction and heart has not stopped completely.

31 PROBLEMS
IN ADDITION TO ACCIDENTS

1. Acne

Embarrassment comes when inflamed sebaceous glands cause pustular eruptions. To mask unsightly blemishes, use a non-greasy cover-up make-up. To get rid of excess oil causing basic problem: (1) wash face four or five times a day with detergent soap; (2) get plenty of sun to encourage peeling; (3) go easy on sweets, fats, greasy products. In extreme cases, sulphur pastes, antibiotics, hormones or artificial peeling by dermatologist may be called for.

2. Alcohol and Other Drug Addiction

Because alcohol results in drunkenness, its use is easy to detect. Not so with other addictions. The first sign that a young person may be "hooked" on drugs is usually a "money bind." The young addict begins to feed his habit by selling things he picks up at home. TV sets, radios and other saleable items begin to disappear. When this happens, the wise parent goes for help.

Most authorities consider marijuana no more harmful than tobacco or alcohol, but at this writing, it is illegal. Turning to it or to alcohol can lead to an arrest for the illegal use of drugs or for drunk driving.

Some drug addiction begins with glue sniffing, diet pills, Methedrine (speed) and ends up with LSD (acid) and/or heroin. "Mainlining" of heroin can cost up to $100 a day and is a killer. Because it is so costly, it also leads to robbery and other crimes.

Preaching does no good for any addiction. If you suspect a young person is addicted to any drug, go to an expert in your town who knows drugs and is sympathetic with kids. (This person may be a policeman, doctor, recreation director or school counselor.) With his help, the young person who really wants to help himself can go to a rehabilitation house. Such centers are free. For alcoholics, Alcoholics Anonymous is best first step.

3. Allergies

By adolescence, tracing is easy when an unusual bronchial or skin flare-up occurs. If you suspect an allergy, put away a new cosmetic or fabric. If the flare-up subsides, you know the trouble. In case of sinus trouble in a new climate, take antihistamines for a few days. If your sinus clears up, a strange plant or dust is probably causing your problem.

4. Anemia

Girls are more apt than boys to have a deficiency in red blood cells containing hemoglobin. Both, however, will be mildly anemic if they are not getting enough iron, protein, vitamins, copper and cobalt. Any young person who is pale, listless, breathless during mild exercise can benefit from more iron. Egg yolks, red meat, sardines, nuts and apricots are good sources. Tomatoes, oranges, lemons and grapefruit which are rich in Vitamin C aid the absorption of iron. Don't spend money for iron tablets unless blood test shows severe anemia. They do no good when anemia is not present and can be upsetting.

5. Cavities

Adolescents have more cavities than any other age group due to sudden body growth and bone enlargement which creates a giant demand for calcium. Often, the teeth are robbed.

Also, adolescents are breakfast skippers. Three helps are (1) milk; (2) an orange instead of a sweet at bedtime; (3) thorough cleansing with a stiff toothbrush and paste (or soda and salt) at bedtime for sure.

6. Cramps While Swimming

Stretching unused muscles causes cramps in fingers, toes, arms, legs; will disappear with a change of position, relaxation of tension or through kneading the affected member. With an abdominal cramp, the swimmer should change position and/or float, if possible.

7. Dandruff

Do not spend money for an expensive dandruff shampoo which can only "wash away flakes." Instead, keep hair and scalp scrupulously clean and free from small flakes of epidermis and excess oil with an inexpensive detergent shampoo. Like acne (with which dandruff is often associated) the condition clears up in time.

8. Diabetes

This is a serious disease in the young adult, characterized by thirst, frequent urination, weakness and loss of weight. It is easy to detect through a urine test, because unused sugar is deposited there. For a free detection examination, ask your local American Diabetes Association where to mail or take a specimen. There is no cure, but the condition can be controlled with diet, exercise and insulin. This endocrine gland disorder runs in families.

9. Excess Fat

Like acne, excess fat can cause emotional problems. Left out of social gatherings and/or a butt of jokes, the fat adolescent consoles himself by eating more and becomes fatter. With diet, exercise and a changed outlook, he can lose pounds but psychological or group help from an organization like Weight Watchers or TOPS may be necessary to ge the program started.

10. Eyestrain

Twitching lids, headache, nausea, moving spots in front of the eyes and an inability to see in some situations may mean glasses are called for. To avoid over-paying for high-fashion frames, shop around. Find the frames you want in any shop, then look in less expensive optical places for the same or similar shape. (You will get your best buy at an optical company with many branches which buys lenses and frames in quantity and can give chain store prices.) Go to a respected eye doctor for your initial examination. Then, carry his prescription with you when traveling, so that you don't have to start from scratch.

11. Fainting Spell

Fainting can mean anemia or low blood pressure but it usually comes when affected person is tired, hungry, starved for food (or for oxygen in stuffy room), or in shock. If you feel a spell coming on, get your head down between your knees to get blood to brain. Put a drop of ammonia on handkerchief and inhale.

12. Goiter

If a diet has been lacking in iodine, a goiter usually shows up by adolescence. The condition is more usual in girls than in boys. While iodized salt prevents goiter, iodine given internally will not cure a goiter but it will prevent one from getting larger. Call doctor's attention to enlarged thyroid gland when you have your checkup.

13. Gonorrhea

A whitish discharge from the penis or vagina along with pain in the abdomen and burning on urination are the first symptoms. Secondary physical problems (i.e., arthritis) can come unless infection is cleared up. Because gonorrhea can be transferred to other members of the family from towels, diapers, etc., a culture should be made of the discharge as soon as it is noticed. For a free laboratory examination, call your state or local public health office about where to go. Penicillin is accepted treatment.

14. Homosexuality

Many boys and girls "fall in love" with a member of their same sex in adolescence, but this sex interest disappears with maturity. Only if the adolescent shows a prolonged attachment to members of the same sex should there be concern. A psychiatrist, whom you can find through your local United Fund or Community Referral Service or through the Psychiatric Clinic at your county hospital or nearby university, can tell you whether treatment is called for. (Usually, through these clinics, you can have a free consultation and pay nothing or according to your means if help is needed.) Studies show that prolonged dressing in ladies clothes and an effeminate manner (as young as 6 to 9) may indicate a homosexual tendency.

15. Malnutrition

Not only the poor are malnourished. Some young people are unable to assimilate a specific food, and others who are away at school may go light on regular meals and fill up between times on high-colorie starches and sweets which are empty of vitamins and minerals. As a result, night blindness may come from a lack of Vitamin A; bleeding gums, from a lack of Vitamin C; anemia, from not having foods rich in iron; tooth decay, from not enough calcium and Vitamin D. Nobody who reads this, however, should rush out for vitamin tablets. Three balanced meals a day are all that is needed to provide proper nourishment.

16. Masturbation

Most doctors agree that 99 percent of all boys masturbate and the other 1 percent who say they don't are liars. Manipulation of one's genitals does not cause mental sickness or physical problems, and usually becomes less frequent, anyway, when a young person learns to relate to a member of the opposite sex in a normal way.

17. Menstrual Abnormalities

If the monthly discharge of blood from the uterus begins earlier than ten or later than 17, it can indicate a glandular disorder. Also, if the menstruation is irregular or profuse or scanty, there may be a endocrine imbalance that can be helped with hormonal therapy.[4]

The girl who has a slight abdominal pain in the first day or two of her period, should think of this as a nuisance, nothing more. If she is in real distress, she can have an examination by a doctor to find out whether her distress is physical or emotional. If emotional, a talk with a psychiatrist, whom she can find through United Fund, can help her to be better adjusted sexually for the rest of her life.

18. Mononucleosis

Diagnosis is made by a blood test for this highly infectious glandular fever, caused by a virus, which is passed from one young adult to another. Symptoms are fever, sore throat, swollen glands, weakness, fatigue. Treatment calls for bed rest until blood test shows no more than usual amount of leukocytes. If convalescence is hurried, a relapse can occur; the patient may be ill for months and, occasionally, the liver can be damaged.

19. Neurotic Symptoms

When a young adult has deep feelings of anxiety about the stresses of normal living, he or she may need professional help. the indicator may be an ulcer, frequent fainting, abrupt high and low cycles, depression, extra long hours of sleep, nervousness, suspiciousness, frequent tears. Do not deal with such emotional reactions with tranquilizers or non-professional analysis, which can do more harm than good. Talk to a school counselor or a local mental health clinic about whether professional help is called for. If so, years of trouble can be avoided with early treatment.

20. Nocturnal Emissions (Wet Dreams)

A boy in adolescence has sex dreams accompanied by nocturnal emission which relieves sexual desires. This simply means the boy is physically ready for parenthood as menstruation indicates the same for a girl.

21. Oily hair and skin[5]

Sebaceous glands are overactive during puberty and release oil which makes for dandruff and/or acne. To prevent both, shampoo hair three or four times a week with a detergent shampoo followed by a diluted vinegar rinse and wash skin twice a day with soap and water. Go easy on creams and wax-make-up and keep comb, brush, wash cloths and towels immaculate. The oily condition disappears with years.

22. Perspiration Odor

Odor, caused by bacteria attracted to ammonia and urea excreted from the sweat glands, is prevented with a daily bath and an inexpensive deodorant which contains alcohol (so is quick drying) and an antibacterial agent to kill germs. Also, shaving the underarms of hair, which retains perspiration, is a help. Do not pay for promotional, secret or made-up ingredients or brand names. There is a difference between a deodorant and an anti-perspirant, neither of which is harmful. The latter usually contains aluminum chlorhydroxide to check excessive sweating. To save money, buy the "store brand" in your grocery store.

23. Poor Posture

Rapid growth, sex embarrassment in girls, poor sitting, standing or walking habits, anxiety, malnutrition and/or reading in poor light can make for poor posture, which can lead to chronic back trouble in later years. Ballet lessons, a modeling course, an outdoor sport (especially swimming) can help an adolescent to stand tall. Naturally, this makes for an improvement in appearance that eliminates self-consciousness.

24. Rheumatoid Arthritis

With this disease, which comes on in young adults,[6] one or two fingers are affected at first and, later, many joints may be hot and swollen. Patient may run a fever and have a general feeling of fatigue. Hands and feet may be numb. Because the condition improves during pregnancy, doctors investigated adrenal steroids which were found to give relief.

Treatment calls for plenty of rest, good food with plenty of iron, vitamins, protein and calcium with aspirin to relieve pain. Critical cases can be helped with Prednisone, U.S.P., which is marketed by a variety of companies in a far-ranging price range. Because the disease is puzzling, patients are inclined to switch doctors and climates, so making treatment for this condition unusually expensive.

If you suspect the disease, do the following: (1) get to a diagnostic clinic to confirm your diagnosis; (2) write to Arthritis Foundation, 1212 Avenue of the Americas, New York City, 10036, for free booklets which will explain the disease and tell you how to relieve and live with this condition; (3) follow common sense directions of a good internist, absolutely refusing to get caught in the "let's try another doctor" trap; (4) get advice from a Mental Health Clinic about the need for psychiatric help. Some patients use arthritis as a crutch to avoid going on with life.

25. Schizophrenia

This mental disease, often appearing in adolescence, is marked by a withdrawl into a dream world. Uncalled for laughter, or tears or other bizarre behavior may take place. Recovery comes if the disease is not of long duration. When someone in your home is disturbed, get to a mental clinic and let a trained person decide what is called for. Don't let parental guilt hold you back from talking finances. Therapy, hospitalization and special drugs can be a monumental expense. Check your hospitalization and/or major medical plan to see that mental illness is covered.

26. Sexual Promiscuity

Most psychiatrists believe that "petting" a contemporary member (or a number of members) of the opposite sex before marriage can make for a more meaningful relationship later. But few recommend promiscuity, and many consider indiscriminate sex relations with many partners a sign of emotional difficulty. There is little a parent can do but *be there,* unless the adolescent is unusually approachable, in which case discussion with a psychologist can be suggested. Most adolescents resist analysis, but enjoy therapy (especially group therapy) once they begin.

27. Smoking

Young people know there is a connection between smoking and lung cancer, heart disease, bronchial disorders and circulatory problems, yet, they smoke anyway through a desire to be "grown up." Do anything, including bribing, to encourage one not to start. Urge adolescents to take part in sports and other activities where smoking is taboo and, above all, become a good model yourself.

28. Tularemia

This disease, characterized by aching, fever, chills and localized swelling, which lasts several weeks, is often contracted by teen agers who may be handling infected rabbits or other animals. To diagnose, an agglutination test must be made. If positive, streptomycin will be given. Because this must be injected and tularemia is long term, learn how to give the required shots if a member of your family has the disease.

29. Tuberculosis

Tubercle bacillus can live in the body of a person who does not have active tuberculosis. Should resistance be lowered by fatigue, overwork, poor diet, etc., the infection will develop. Symptoms are fever, spitting, night sweats, fatigue and, in a later stage, spitting blood.

If you suspect tuberculosis, go to a clinic for an X-ray. Treatment today does not call for a sanitarium, which used to be costly and long term, but it does call for bed rest while the infection is active.

Powerful drugs like INH (isoniazid), streptomycin and PAS, another organic chemical, have reduced fatalities, but recovery can take time, so talk to your examining physician about how to save money—at home, in a sanitarium and especially in the purchase of drugs. The ones named here are not perishable and should be purchased in quantity.

30. Undeveloped Sex Organs

Special hormones can be given to a boy if the testes are child-like or remain in the scrotal sac. If the boy is a true eunuch, hormones may have to be taken for life, but he can live normally.

Hormone treatment is advised for girls if body hair, late breast development and menstruation do not occur naturally until they are 17 or 18.

31. Underweight

There is no need to worry about an adolescent's lack of pounds
unless he is listless, lacks vitality and gets frequent infections. See
that he or she gets plenty of iron, protein, calcium, vitamins and
minerals in a three-meals-a-day program, and forget about weight.
Frame sizes vary, and some young people are more active than
others.

Emotional problems that come to all adolescents pass, but
attitudes and habits acquired by a boy or girl in this period can
affect his or her future. Parents should stand by. A well adjusted
adult will be the reward.

---

[1] The highest number of fatalities in automobile accident occur in drivers under 21.

[2] One insurance company reports that at least one of the drivers involved in close to
100% of all fatal highway accidents has been drinking. And New York health authorities
report that heroin addiction is the leading cause of death of New Yorkers between 15
and 30.

[3] In most cases, inflating the lungs by breathing into the victim's mouth is easier and
more effective.

[4] This requires a doctor's prescription.

[5] See page 00 for complete explanation of skin.

[6] Comes to girls and women three times as often as to boys and men.

WHAT TO DO WHEN A STRICKEN PERSON CAN'T TALK

Symptoms before unconscious state	Probable trouble	What to do
1. Severe pain under breastbone extending left to arm and neck. Profuse perspiration. Shortness of breath.	Acute heart attack.	Prop patient up to 45 degree angle. Give nothing unless patient's history calls for medication. Don't transport. Wait for ambulance.
2. Mental confusion changing to coma. Flushed face. Deep, noisy breathing. Full pulse. High blood pressure. Paralysis on one or both sides of body. Incontinence.	Stroke.	Keep patient flat, turning on side to allow for drooling. No food, liquid or medication unless doctor advises.
3. Vomiting, abdominal pain, air hunger, heavy breathing. Eyeballs, soft; skin, dry. Breath has sweetish odor.	Diabetic coma.	Get diabetic to swallow sugar or candy. Transport to hospital.

4. Convulsive movement of body, brief unconsciousness.	Epileptic attack.	Try to pad patient but don't put any thing in mouth. You will be bitten. Turn to allow for drooling. Wait for seizure to end.
5. Deep sleep, probably in bed.	Overdose of sleeping pills.	Force liquids, induce vomiting, transport patient to hospital. If poison is strychnine, do not move forcibly; convulsions will result.
6. Deep sleep, person reeks of liquor, perspires excessively.	Alcoholic stupor.	Give fruit juice, gingerale or milk, if wanted; allow patient to sleep it off.
7. Numb and drowsy in extreme cold.	Freezing to death.	Bring victim in, give artificial respiration, put feet in warm water, wrap in blankets, give warm liquid.
8. Weakness after hot sun, exhaustion, dry skin, nausea, fever.	Sunstroke.	Bed rest. Give fluid containing salt, tepid baths and create draft to get temperature down. Call doctor if temperature stays high.
9. Loss of consciousness resulting from stuffiness in room, bad news or loss of blood.	Fainting spell.	Lay patient flat or try to get head down below knees.

8

133 Get Well Recipes for Adults Who Are Injured or Ill

The best way to get more mileage out of your medical care dollar is to stay healthy; the second best way is to know what to do about a specific upset. Here is a consensus recommendation by top doctors for 133 major and minor injuries and illnesses which bring an American man and/or woman into a general practitioner's office.

Advice given here is no short order course in medicine designed to eliminate the need for a doctor forevermore. *True, it will help you to avoid spending money for a doctor when you can do as well on your own.* At the same time, it will help you (1) know what to do when a doctor can't be reached; (2) assess your condition so that you can save time (and money) at the doctor's office by talking only in facts; (3) know how to relieve pain and prevent complications while waiting for a doctor.

Symptom or Problem	Cause or What It Means	What to do
1. *Abdominal Pain*		
Cramps accompanied by nausea and diarrhea.	Often caused by nervousness, anger, fear.	If you habitually over-react to frustration, get psychological help. Otherwise, ask yourself what's the matter (the visit of a disliked relative, anger at a mate's extravagance, worry about a child). Take an aspirin and a little soda in water (or Maalax) and get a good night's sleep.
Low pain and wind after a meal, white gelatine-like mucous in feces. '	Intestinal inflammation (colitis).	Take vitamins but avoid raw fruits and vegetables; eat bland diet; get away for vacation.
Severe pain around navel which shifts to lower right side, plus nausea.	Appendicitis.	Operation is only cure.
Sudden severe pain several hours after eating, abdominal tenderness, vomiting, headache, cold perspiration.	Food poisoning, especially if several who have eaten together are affected.	Bed rest, along with small amounts of ginger ale or Coke. No solid food until recovery. Discuss condition with doctor by telephone. He will probably prescribe Atropine Sulfate.
Abdominal pain, plus vomiting and diarrhea, along with "cold," sore throat, headache.	Intestinal flu; "the bug."	Bed rest, lots of liquids, little food. Runs course in two days.
Pain in upper abdomen; blood is vomited.	May be ulcer or cancer.	Get to doctor at once.

Symptom or Problem	Cause or What It Means	What to do
Belt of pain around abdomen below ribs, with pain by right shoulder. May be agonizing. Profuse sweating.	Gall bladder problem, passage of stones.	Gall bladder may have to be removed. Sedation necessary while stones are passed.
Pain in lower abdomen, back and thighs. Woman may pass blood clot.	Miscarriage, polyp, cancer.	Call doctor.
Pain in side or back radiating to lower part of abdomen, genitals and inner thigh with pain on urination; and blood in urine usually present.	Kidney stone.	Call doctor who will prescribe pain reliever and lots of fluids, a special diet; may operate.
Constant stomach pain, no appetite, weight loss, abdominal distension.	Cancer.	Surgery, the sooner the better.

2. *Accidents*

This is the number four killer in the United States and the number one killer for adults, 34 to 45. On the next two double pages you will find visual explanations of eight of the principal types of accidents with instructions for what to do *first* in each category.

Many accidents result in shock. Knowing what to do when there is a sudden loss of vitality resulting from fear, pain and/or loss of blood can save a life. As you wait for help to come after any accident, follow these simple directions indicated in Figure 8-1.

NUMBER ONE KILLER
MOTOR VEHICLE ACCIDENT

Motor vehicle accidents (involving people in automobiles and/or pedestrians) account for close to half of our accidental deaths each year. First step, after seeing the victim is out of way of oncoming

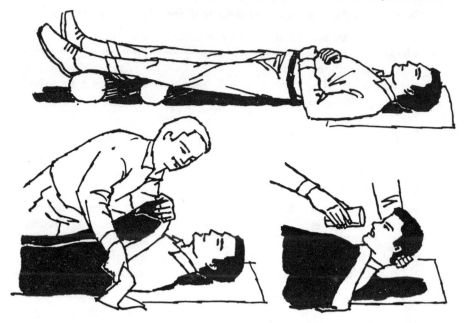

Figure 8-1

Prone Figure: Keep patient flat. Unless he has head injury, raise feet (on logs, pillows, rolled newspapers) above head.

Man with Blanket: To prevent patient from becoming cold, cover with blanket unless weather is hot.

Water Glass: If patient is conscious, let him sip water. Stay nearby to give assurance.

traffic, is to call 0 for Operator. Wherever you are, she will get state police, ambulance and alert hospital. Give her exact instructions as to whereabouts. For specific instructions for caring for victim who may be dying from loss of blood, see page 93.

NUMBER TWO KILLER
FALLS

The majority of home falls are suffered by women, and when serious results come, 3/4 are in the over 65. Most could be prevented with better lighting, more careful attention to detail. If

Figure 8-2: Number One Killer, Motor Vehicle Accident

Motor vehicle accidents (involving people in automobiles and/or pedestrians) account for close to half of our accidental deaths each year. First step, after seeing the victim is out of way of oncoming traffic, is to call O for Operator. Wherever you are, she will get state police, ambulance and alert hospital. Give her exact instructions as to whereabouts. For specific instructions for caring for victim who may be dying from loss of blood, see page 93.

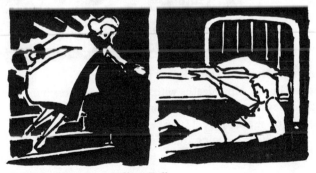

Figure 8-3: Number Two Killer, Falls

In the Home: The majority of home falls are suffered by women, and when serious results come, 3/4 are in the over 65. Most could be prevented with better lighting, more careful attention to detail. If possible, get someone to call for ambulance while you give first aid for shock, see page 110. Place head on pillow so that secretions can drain from mouth.

From Bed—by an ill adult (or a baby who may be in your care)

When man (or woman) falls and is knocked unconscious, never try to "jostle him awake." Also, do not move unconscious person, even if lightweight. Keep unconscious person absolutely quiet until ambulance comes.

possible, get someone to call for ambulance while you give first aid for shock, see previous page. Place head on pillow so that secretions can drain from mouth.

When man (or woman) falls and is knocked unconscious, never try to "jostle him awake." Also, do not move unconscious person, even if lightweight. Keep unconscious person absolutely quiet until ambulance comes.

NUMBER THREE KILLER
BURNS

Most deaths within a few days after a thermal burn come from shock. Alleviate pain, quench thirst if patient can swallow, and give first aid for shock, page 110.

Figure 8-4: Number Three Killer, Burns
Thermal Burns: Most deaths within a few days after burn come from shock. Alleviate pain, quench thirst if patient can swallow, and give first aid for shock, page 110. **Chemical Burns:** First step, wash away lye, acid, alkali, cleaning fluid with large quantities of water. Read label for instructions for specific burn. Give first aid for shock.

For a chemical burn, wash away lye, acid, alkali, cleaning fluid with large quantities of water. Read label for instructions for specific burn. Give first aid for shock.

NUMBER FOUR KILLER
DROWNING

Pick any foreign matter out of throat but don't waste time trying to empty lungs of water. Immediately give mouth-to-mouth resuscitation. (See page 94)

Figure 8-5: Number Four Killer, Drowning

When Swimming: Don't waste time trying to get water out of lungs. Give mouth-to-mouth resuscitation, see page 94. **In the Bathtub:** Pick any foreign matter out of throat but don't waste time trying to empty lungs of water. Give mouth-to-mouth resuscitation at once.

NUMBER FIVE KILLER
FIREARMS

If wound is in chest or in abdomen, keep patient on back, giving nothing by mouth. All gunshot wounds must go to hospital even if

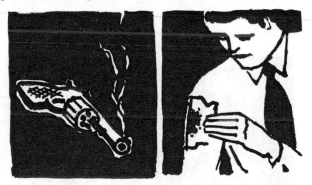

Figure 8-6: Number Five Killer, Firearms

Gunshot Wound: If wound is in chest or in abdomen, keep patient on back, giving nothing by mouth. All gunshot wounds must go· to hospital even if not bleeding immediately. If patient is bleeding profusely, put pressure on wound as advised on page 93, while another calls hospital. **Powder Burns:** Accidental explosion of gun or explosive can carry powder and dirt into skin. If flesh is charred, rush patient to hospital for antitoxin.

not bleeding immediately. If patient is bleeding profusely, put pressure on wound as advised on page 93, while another calls hospital.

Firearms patient should have antitoxin in hospital.

Figure 8-7: Number Six Killer, Machinery

At Home: First step: prevent hemorrhage by applying pressure. Then, treat for shock. **On the Job:** Faulty machinery is killer on farms and in factories. Rush injured worker to hospital or first aid station in factory. Use wads of cloth (torn shirt, etc.) on wound or as pressure pad.

Figure 8-8: Number Seven Killer, Poison Gases

Carbon Monoxide: When fire strikes, carbon monoxide can cause death as readily as burns. Get unconscious victim out of enclosed room into fresh air. **Benzol or Other Fume-Maker:** Fumes can cause unconsciousness. Get victim into open air and call ambulance for oxygen tank.

NUMBER SIX KILLER
MACHINERY

First step: prevent hemorrhage by applying pressure. Then treat for shock.

Faulty machinery is killer on farms and in factories. Rush injured worker to hospital or first aid station in factory. Use wads of cloth (torn shirt, etc.) on wound or as pressure pad.

NUMBER SEVEN KILLER
POISON GASES

When fire strikes, carbon monoxide can cause death as readily as burns. Get unconscious victim out of enclosed room into fresh air.

Fumes from benzol can cause unconsciousness. Get victim into open air and call ambulance for oxygen tank.

Figure 8-9: Number Eight Killer, Internal Poisons

Accidental Swallowing: One-third of all children's deaths are caused by the swallowing of poison. For them or for adults, your aim should be to (1) get poison out of stomach by inducing vomiting; (2) slow down absorption of poison by giving fluids. **Near Suicide:** For overdose of barbituates, induce vomiting, give large quantities of black coffee along with water.

NUMBER EIGHT KILLER
INTERNAL POISONS

One-third of all children's deaths are caused by the swallowing of poison. For them or for adults, your aim should be to (1) get poison out of stomach by inducing vomiting; (2) slow down absorption of poison by giving fluids.

For overdose of barbiturates, induce vomiting, give large quantities of black coffee along with water.

Symptom or Problem	Cause or What It Means	What to do
3. *Addison's Disease*		
Patient is weak, has low blood pressure, dark colored skin.	A one-time fatal disease due to underfunctioning of adrenal glands.	When diagnosis is sure doctor can give replacement therapy of Cortisone.
4. *Alcoholism* [1]		
	The chronic drinker with a psychic dependence on alcohol usually is a poor eater, so other physical conditions like malnutrition (and often diseases like cirrhosis of the liver, eye problems, poor resistence to pneumonia, etc.) may be present.	Psychic rehabilitation plus treatment for secondary diseases is called for. The drug, Antabuse, which causes violent reaction to alcohol, makes for aversion; Alcoholics Anonymous[2] provides help through group aid, psychotherapy may get at root of cause. During days after immediate withdrawal, hospitalization may be needed.
5. *Amputation*		
Accidental or surgical removal of limb, arm, finger, toe, etc.	An arm or leg or finger may be cut off in a rail, plane or car accident. Your quick action in applying pressure on the bleeding artery may save a life.	In case of accident, your knowing how to apply pressure on the artery may save a life. After ·surgical amputation, psychological help may be recommended.
6. *Anemia*		
a. Acute		
A disease more common to women than to men in	Loss of blood from a serious wound, bleeding ulcer, hemorrhoids, ex-	When hemorrhage is massive, shock will probably accompany

Symptom or Problem	Cause or What It Means	What to do
which red blood cells containing hemoglobin are below normal. Patient is pale, short of breath, may be faint and have other evidence of heart failure.	cessive menstrual flow or cancer of the stomach or intestines may cause acute anemia. Also, a faulty diet plus chronic bleeding from one of the above causes can lead to severe anemia.	anemia. *Rush patient to emergency section of hospital* for transfusion to replace lost blood. When chronic blood loss from some cause other than massive hemorrhage causes anemia, diagnostic tests should be made.[3]
b. Pernicious Same as above but as common in men as in women; usually hits the over-40 who are plump or prematurely grey.	Patient's gait is wobbly, skin is pale, tongue is lemon colored. (Bone marrow and blood tests will determine whether disease is present.)	Injections of liver or B12 bring about dramatic improvement. Treatment must be continued for life.

7. *Aneurysm*

Bulge like a weakened spot on an inner tube in the wall of the artery, often on the aorta, caused by a weakening of the vessel wall.	Extreme pain caused by pressure on surrounding organs.	Slowed down life, rest, sedatives for pain. If patient can stand an operation, the weakened spot can be "mended" by surgery.

8. *Appendicitis*

Inflammation of the appendix, which is a hollow tube extending from the first part of the large intestine. Two types are usually named.		
a. Acute	Abdominal pain in the appendix area, nausea, chills, vomiting, mild fever.	The tube becomes plugged; drainage cannot take place; infection results as with a boil.

Symptom or Problem	Cause or What It Means	What to do
		Should the pus-filled appendix burst, peritonitis can result and the patient may die. Today, antibiotics can prevent death but, still, a ruptured appendix is a serious problem so when an appendix becomes inflamed, an operation is recommended.
b. Chronic Repeated attacks of acute appendicitis.	Diagnosis is often confused with kidney, intestinal, ovarian and gall bladder disorders. Actually, there is no such thing as chronic appendicitis. If there are repeated attacks, the attacks are acute.	If the appendix is inflamed one time or over and over, the only cure is removal.
9. *Hardening of the Arteries (sometimes called arteriosclerosis)*		
Loss of elasticity of artery walls, with linings becoming weakened, and cholesterol deposits forming clots on uneven surfaces, so that arteries are narrowed and blood does not get through to various body parts (brain, lungs, heart). Condition may cause stroke, Parkinson's	Slower thinking may indicate clogged arteries leading to brain; pain in chest may indicate hardening of arteries near heart; pain in limbs may indicate arteries to lower legs are affected.	No known cure-all, but synthetic tubing is sometimes used today to replace clogged arteries. Best cure is prevention of further clogging. Low cholesterol can slow down hardening—exercise helps—cutting out smoking is aid. If arteries are already affected, slower life style automatically accompanies slower blood flow.

Symptom or Problem	Cause or What It Means	What to do
disease, coronary problems, kidney disease, pain in chest, thyroid problems, diabetes.		
10. *Arthritis*[4]		
Inflammation of the joints from one of many causes.		
a. Rheumatoid Arthritis Occurs in young adults, usually before 42, and in women far more often than in men. Now thought to be a "collagen" disease, one that affects tissues in joints.	Swelling usually starts in hand, joints are red, shiny, hot. Patient feels run-down, tired, may run low fever.	Bed rest with physiotherapy, plus a buildup diet and aspirin, which is still the main standby for relieving pain here as for other types of arthritis. In extreme cases, cortisone is recommended, mostly to relieve pain.
b. Rheumatoid Arthritis of the Spine Occurs in men far more often than in women, hits in their 30s and 40s	Chronic backache and stiffness which gradually bends body forward and down.	X-ray sometimes helpful; aspirin for pain; exercise; posture correction in daily work.
c. Osteoarthritis A disease, occurring after 40, in which bony bumps appear at joints and interfere with ordinary movements. Pain is likened to a toothache. A consequence of aging and very common.	Wear and tear on joints, poor posture, strain from overwork.	Aspirin to relieve joint pains; easing up of postural strain; massage and/or physiotherapy; bedboard if spine is affected.

Symptom or Problem	Cause or What It Means	What to do
11. *Asphyxia*		
Loss of consciousness due to lack of oxygen and excess of carbon dioxide in the blood.	May be accidental due to victim's breathing air containing insufficient oxygen or toxic gas. Leaking gas in a home or confined place where gas-driven machine is being run, or lack of oxygen in a sewer, mine or silo can be cause. Or deliberate suicide attempt may cause unconsciousness.	In gas-filled room, shut off gas before attempting rescue; in cave, have others tie rope around you before you go to aid. Get victim into open air as soon as possible and begin artificial respiration (pg. 95) while someone calls the fire department and an oxygen tank. Help the patient to exhale and inhale until oxygen tank arrives
12. *Asthma*[5]		
A disorder of respiration, often allergy-caused, characterized by wheezing and feeling of constriction in the chest. A first attack can come at any age, but tendency to asthma is usually recognized before middle adulthood. Due to constriction of the bronchiole.	Attack begins suddenly; patient has difficulty breathing; turns blue; pulse becomes weak. Onset may follow emotional strain or may be allergy-produced. (Because of heart failure and/or obstruction of the windpipe can cause similar symptoms, a doctor must be depended on for diagnosis.)	What about your environment? Do you have a new pet (canary, parakeet, cat, long-haired dog or some other animal never near before) or are you using a new face powder? Have you eaten foods never eaten before? Are you living in new climate? Have you been under tremendous strain? Obviously, each demands a different remedy. One effective medication for immediate relief is the bronchodilator, Ephedrine Sulfate, U.S.P., (made from a Chinese herb centuries old). This must be given with a doctor's prescription.

Symptom or Problem   **Cause or What It Means**   **What to do**

13. *Backache*

Pain in the back, usually confined to the lumbar region.	Pain may be caused by inflammation of ligaments which bind small bones in spine together; long-time postural stress, a slipped disc; spinal arthritis; · strain from unequal length of legs or flat feet or by kidney, intestinal or menstrual disorders.	Take aspirin, get a hard mattress to keep spine straight, take posture-correcting exercises. When distress is severe, a back or neck brace may be needed until acute phase is over. Buy through a discount store.

14. *Baldness*

A scalp which is destitute of hair. An inherited condition, far more common in males than in females, although a few women do lose their hair naturally, and women as well as men can become bald as a result of disease.	Natural baldness occurs to some degree in half of all men, and is a virility sign. (Baldness comes when the male's beard is fully developed and his sex hormone is at its highest level.) A woman's hair may thin after menopause, which also suggests a hormone cause.	When baldness occurs naturally, there is no way to stop it. However, after a debilitating disease, hair often comes in again as vitality is restored.

15. *Barber's Itch*

Infection of the bearded area of the face.	Caused by ringworm or staphylococcus germ transferred by contaminated razor.	Apply Whitfield's ointment for ringworm, take Penicillin G, U.S.P., for "staph" infection.

16. *Bladder Trouble*[6]

An infection or inflammation of the "elastic" pouch which holds water passed from the	Colon bacilli germ frequently infects bladder, but others do same. Inactive and elderly people most suscept-	Take urine specimen to clinic or doctor who will prescribe Sulfisaxazole, U.S.P., if analysis and/or urine culture in-

Symptom or Problem	Cause or What It Means	What to do
kidneys through the ureters. Medical name: cystitis.	ible. An enlarged prostate gland is trouble source, and stones from kidneys passed through ureters (20 times more common in men than in women) can cause extreme pain. Any bladder disorder should be looked into immediately; tumor which causes bleeding can be cured but is serious.	dicates infection. If problem persists, your doctor will look into bladder with cystoscope, feel prostate gland with finger placed in rectum, X-ray.

17. Boils

A painful sore caused by microbic infection which often has its beginning in hair follicle and may occur in diabetics.	Weakened resistance to infection, friction plus grime on shirt collar, staphylococcus infection lurking in nose or ear or other recess.	Never squeeze a carbuncle (a deep-seated boil-like abscess) and never open a boil above the upper lip which can lead (and has led) to brain infection. Do put applications (as hot as you can stand) on the boil which brings a clean supply of blood to fight infection. If boil does not drain in a day or two, go to doctor for lancing and take Penicillin G, U.S.P., to get rid of infection. Then, build up resistance with a well-balanced diet plus fresh air and exercise.

18. Brain Tumor

New growth in brain.	Headache which may awaken patient at night; irritability; personality change; weak-	If worried, explain headache symptoms by telephone to doctor. He can make examination

Symptom or Problem **Cause or What It Means** **What to do**

ness; balance trouble; visual problem.

for tumors, if he believes this is necessary. Both benign and malignant tumors can be removed surgically.

19. *Lump in Breast*

A lump which can be felt and/or seen and may or may not be painful.

Several types of lumps: fibroidenosis, rarely painful, usually comes after 40; rounded cyst, any age, rarely painful; abscess, usually occurs during breast feeding, very painful; harmless tumor, any age, usually not painful; cancerous tumor, any age, usually not painful.

Learn to palpate your own breasts for a dominant lump. Call a doctor the minute you feel such a lump because X-rays of the breast and a biopsy may be needed. If a lump proves to be cancer, the faster you have care, the better. And if the tumor should be harmless, the more relieved you will be to find out.

20. *Breathlessness*

Sometimes called "shortness of breath"—a feeling of a need for more air when you do things you formerly could do quite comfortably.

A gasping for breath is a sign that your blood does not have the red cells it needs to carry oxygen to all parts of your body or that your heart is not pumping blood fast enough to supply your body's needs or that something is blocking the flow of oxygen to your lungs or from your lungs to your liver and muscles where food is broken down. Never disregard breathlessness, especially if you are being awakened in the night

If your breathlessness comes from overweight or from smoking or drinking too much, cut down on food, tobacco and/or alcohol, and step up your daily exercise. Cut down on fats and sweets in your diet and eat more iron-rich foods, named in footnote on page (Anemia often causes breathlessness.) A change will come in weeks.

If you are not over-eating, over-smoking or over-drinking, have a

Symptom or Problem	Cause or What It Means	What to do
	by a gasping need for air.	complete examination which includes a blood test for anemia, heart examination, chest and larynx X-ray and tests for emphysema and asthma. Any one may be cause, and will take special treatment. (See separate headings.)

21. *Radiation and/or Hot Water Burns*

Burns from hot water bags, hot showers, heat lamps, etc.	After repeated applications of heat, the nerves in the skin become numb, do not notice burn; also with age, tissues of the body become less resistant to heat.	Whether preparing a hot water bottle, infrared lamp, foot bath, electric pad for yourself or another, consider age and peculiar sensitivity of patient, and *go easy.* (Easy check: if it's too hot for you to pick up with your bare hands, it's too hot for any other part of your body or another's.) In case of burn, never pull stuck cloth away from skin, give aspirin, liquid and treat patient for shock.

22. *Bursitis*[7]

Inflammation of the bursa, "oiling" sac between the tendon and bone in a joint.	Top of shoulder, back of shoulder blades, the elbow, hip, knee, really any joint, can become irritated, infected or bruised, at which time the bursa may fill with more than the average amount of fluid. This makes for pain when in motion.	Relieve pain with aspirin, rest, hot baths, showers or local hot water compresses, and careful massage. If pain continues, talk to a doctor about Prednisone, U.S.P., to be given orally, or Hydrocortisone injected directly into the bursa.

Symptom or Problem   **Cause or What It Means**   **What to do**

23. *Cancer*

America's second major killer, next to heart disease. Definition: A malignant blight that starts in moist protective tissue in a body cavity or organ or skin and which spreads, if not arrested, to other parts of the body by way of blood cells and lymphatics.

Seven signs of cancer:
1. Lump in breast, or on lip or tongue.
2. Blood in urine or stool or from nipple or other body opening.
3. Sore on tongue, lip, skin or anywhere that does not heal.
4. Change in color or size of mole or birthmark.
5. Loss of appetite; persistent indigestion.
6. Change in bowel habits.
7. Hoarseness, cough, difficulty in swallowing.

Like a weed, cancer can be uprooted easily when first detected but spreads rapidly if unchecked. Go immediately to a cancer clinic or experienced throat or rectal specialist or urologist or gynecologist or other experienced man in the area where you need attention. But if you are unable to get appointment you want, get to a nearby doctor *at once*. Your examination will probably include X-ray and blood tests and may include a biopsy of tissue and the "Pap" vaginal smear test and mammography (a relatively new type of X-ray test that can detect malignant tumors in the breast before they can be felt by hand). Examination of a suspicious condition may be made through a bronchoscope, proctoscope or cystoscope or other viewing apparatus. Cancer is not "catching" and can be eliminated today through surgery, X-ray, radium, cobalt, and in some cases, through the use of specific medi-

Symptom or Problem	Cause or What It Means	What to do
		cines, hormones and chemicals. Avoid "quack" overnight cures, which *never* work, and be constantly on the lookout for danger signals.

24. *Cataracts*

Symptom or Problem	Cause or What It Means	What to do
Opaque deposits which form on the outer layer of the lens of the eye, impairing vision.	Especially common in the eyes of the elderly although cataracts do form on eyes of young people, too.	It is no longer necessary to wait for cataracts to "ripen" before removal, but any eye operation, no matter how simple, calls for skill, so go to an experienced ophthalmologist for advice and/or surgery. In some cases, cataracts can be treated without surgery.

25. *Cauliflower Ears*

Symptom or Problem	Cause or What It Means	What to do
Ears that have been deformed from repeated injury, resulting in irregular thickening of scar tissue.	Bleeding under skin of ear makes for hardening; to avoid, blood should be drawn off with a needle before hardening occurs.	After ears have become deformed, the thickened substance can be removed by plastic surgery. Most deformities can be corrected today, so inner suffering because of a physical deformity is not necessary. Get to your nearest orthopedic clinic or specialist for advice and/or the name of someone near you who does this work.

26. *Cervicitis*

Symptom or Problem	Cause or What It Means	What to do
Inflammation of the cervix. Usual	May be caused by tears during childbirth, gon-	For simple discharge, douche with 3 tbs. of

Symptom or Problem	Cause or What It Means	What to do
first symptom: leucorrhea (white discharge). Secondary symptoms may be unpleasant odor, itching, nervousness, bleeding and, occasionally, pain.	orrhea, syphilis, polyps, cancer, uterine congestion due to heart problems, microorganisms, which come from the feces, small cervical polyps, aging tissues or a urine infection.	vinegar in two quarts of warm water. If the discharge does not clear up in three or four days, your cervix may be inflamed and probably should be cauterized in the office of a gynecologist, which is not painful. Or you may have a polyp or growth which will have to be removed. If there is atrophy of the tissues, your doctor may prescribe estrogen hormone in suppository or pill form. He may also prescribe phenobarbital if your vaginal problem is causing extreme nervousness. If pain or bleeding is present, douching will not clear up condition. Go to your doctor at once.

27. Chancroid

An infectious venereal ulcer with a soft base. (The chancre is a sore with a hard base.)	Cause is intercourse with an infected person. Chancroid begins as blister five or six days after intercourse, changes to ulcer which is tender, may bleed.	Whatever the circumstances of your infection, do not let guilt keep you from seeing a doctor. He is not there to moralize. He will probably recommend streptomycin injections for a week and salt water baths and/or douches for a few days until sore disappears.

Symptom or Problem	Cause or What It Means	What to do

28. *Childbirth and/or Childbirth Complications*

At time of childbirth: In 95 out of 100 births, the baby comes head first, but in four out of 100 times, the baby comes feet first (breech position) and in one out of 100 times, it lies crosswise and has to be turned in the womb before birth. Low forceps are used frequently in uncomplicated deliveries. And in a few cases, the doctor must use high forceps during a difficult delivery. Today, most doctors prefer to remove the baby through the abdomen by caesarean section if birth will be extremely difficult.

In a few cases, the baby comes without warning; then, anyone near may be called upon to render obstetrical service.

Prenatal care tells the woman and her doctor what to expect. For this reason, prenatal examinations are of utmost importance.

Should you be called upon to give obstetrical help, let baby arrive naturally.

Then, do the following:

(1) Remove mucous from mouth of baby with clean handkerchief and hold upside down and smack on soles of feet to induce breathing.

(2) Tie cord about six inches from baby's navel with clean white twine.

(3) Make a second tie two inches closer to mother and cut cord between ties with sterile scissors.

(4) Wrap breathing baby in blanket and place on side in warm place.

(5) If no doctor comes immediately, await delivery of placenta or afterbirth. After placenta is delivered, massage uterus by placing hand on abdomen and

Symptom or Problem   Cause or What It Means   What to do

rubbing dome of uterus. This action helps the uterus to clamp down and prevent bleeding.

Even if seemingly well, both the baby and the mother should be seen by a doctor and probably taken to a hospital. There, the baby's eyes will be treated with silver nitrate solution to offset any possible gonorrheal infection, the right diet will be prescribed, and the baby will be put into an incubator, if premature.

Tears in the mother's vagina due to rapid expulsion will be repaired and she will be given and enema if needed.

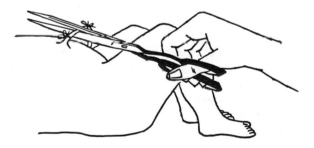

Figure 8-10: Tie cord with twine in two places about six inches from baby's navel—and cut between ties with sterile scissors.

After childbirth:

Mastitis (infection of the breast). Puer-

When milk comes in, breasts may become inflamed, sore and in

Breasts may be pumped and Penicillin will be prescribed. If an abscess

Symptom or Problem	Cause or What It Means	What to do
peral fever (streptococcal infection of the lining of the uterus). Rare in aseptic delivery rooms.	some cases, infected.	has formed, it may have to be drained, but this is rare.

29. *Choking Spell*

A gasping for breath due to a piece of food or foreign object's being lodged in windpipe.	Common to older people due to loose dentures, inadequate mastication or carelessness.	Bend victim head down over a rail; let gravity plus coughing dislodge food. Do not try to pull food out with your fingers unless all else fails. To prevent death, you may have to cut windpipe below obstructed place to let in air.

30. *Cholera*

An epidemic disease in India and China characterized by diarrhea, vomiting, cramps.	Not native to United States; common where people bathe in water polluted with feces.	Take extreme care when traveling in countries where cholera is known; if infected, get to any hospital.

31. *Circulatory Problems*[8]

Any interruption in the 60-second circuit of the 11 pints of blood that carry oxygen, nutrients and waste to various parts of your body can cause disturbances which make for "circulatory problems."	Poor circulation may produce swelling of the ankles, headaches, weakness, numbness of hands or feet, fainting, cold extremities, breathlessness, blue lips, dizziness. The cause and result of poor circulation are interrelated. The patient may have heart disease, high blood pressure,	Get rid of extra weight, stop smoking, exercise and go easy on coffee, alcohol and other stimulants. Above all, have a complete examination at once. If an infection or organic problem is uncovered, follow general rules for improving circulation as you work to erase the specific disturbance or disease

Symptom or Problem   **Cause or What It Means**   **What to do**

kidney disease, diabetes, hardening of the arteries, or may have suffered a stroke. Sometimes, no disease is present when the symptoms appear. If so, consider such symptoms a "warning signal." | which is aggravating your overall problem.

32. *Colitis*

Inflammation of the colon, which is the section of the large intestine extending from the cecum pouch to the rectum at the bottom. Two types of colitis, not related, are ordinary colitis and ulcerative colitis.

Ordinary colitis is a nervous disease, more apt to affect women than men. Onset is characterized by bouts of diarrhea and constipation, abdominal pain, flatulence and the passage of whitish "gelatine" in the stool. Ulcerative colitis is an ulcer in the colon, much more serious than ordinary colitis, occurring in young adults (again, in females more often than in males), marked by severe pain, blood and mucous in stool, fever.

If in great distress, have your colon examined through a sigmoidoscope. With ordinary colitis, the examination will show nothing other than evidence of a nervous spasm, but the ulcerative colitis will reveal ulcers. For the first, a session with a psychotherapist may do more good than medicines, because this disease is usually a sign of an emotional upset or nervous strain. The ulcerative disease is more serious, may call for an operation and certainly a special diet with little roughage but adequate vitamins and minerals plus Prednisone, U.S.P., and antibiotics, namely, Asulfidine.

33. *Common Cold*

A respiratory viral infection character-

A virus is the actual cause of a cold. In addi-

Rest, until fever is gone. Take liquids to

Symptom or Problem	Cause or What It Means	What to do
ized by catarrh, sneezing, sore throat, coughing.	tion, there is an allergic response by the nasal mucous membrane.	offset loss of body liquids through perspiration and droplets lost when sneezing, coughing, running nose, etc. Take aspirin to relieve pain of headache, sore throat and to bring down temperature. There is *no* medication which will kill cold viruses because not one but many viruses can cause these symptoms. Symptomatic therapy is all that is needed. The wanton use of antibiotics for colds is to be condemned since drugs have side effects and their use in conditions which they cannot help may cause allergy and thus prevent their use when needed.

34. *Cold Sores*

A small cluster of sacs or cysts on or around mouth usually accompanied by a cold or fever.	Caused by Herpes simplex which stays in the body for life. Any change (sunburn or chemical change during menstrual cycle) allows it to flare up. It is not serious.	Any inexpensive preparation containing camphor or ether will keep cold sore dry so that a scab can form.

35. *Constipation*

A condition in the bowels when the feces are too hard to pass and evacuation is difficult and infrequent.	Sudden constipation may be due to stricture (narrowing of intestines), blockage by a tumor or cancer.[9] Usually, it is due to a	Unless the problem is severe, comes on suddenly, and/or you have change in the calibre of stools and/or blood in the stool, do not worry

Symptom or Problem   **Cause or What It Means**   **What to do**

| | change of daily evacuation habits when traveling or during an emotional upset. | about missing a bowel movement on an occasional day. Don't resort to physics and enemas to encourage "regularity."[10] Go to the toilet for your bowel movement at a regular time each morning, get plenty of fruits, vegetables, bread, cereals and oils in your daily diet, drink eight glasses of liquid a day and do some exercise. Then, forget your bowels unless you have acute distress. |

36. *Coronary*[11]

| An occlusion in which there is blockage of the coronary arterial branch by a blood clot or fat plaque, thus stopping the flow of blood to part of the heart. | The clot usually occurs within the wall of a vessel at a site narrowed by arteriosclerosis, and the "attack" is accompanied by severe pain. | If patient is in intense pain, do not rush him to the hospital in a private car; keep him lying flat until ambulance arrives. Then, he will probably go directly to the intensive care unit where 24-hour attention is given, and oxygen, nurses, antibloodclotting medicines, pain relievers and intensive professional care and heart machines are available. (Vital statistic: Once past the first 30 days of good care, the long-term outlook is excellent.) Otherwise, even though you may be well in- |

Symptom or Problem	Cause or What It Means	What to do
		sured, don't insist on the biggest private room for "the man of the house," who may be faced with a long period of recuperation and loss of earnings. Worry about finances can aggravate his heart condition. Help him to relax by keeping expenses down.

37. *Smoker's Cough*

Early morning cough usually produces sputum or phlegm. This symptom can also signify a major respiratory problem. Have examination to detect emphysema or lung cancer.	The lining of the cigarette smoker's bronchial tube becomes irritated; more mucous is secreted; coughing results.	*Quit smoking!* Smoker's cough can be a forerunner to lung cancer, chronic bronchitis and/or heart disease, so quit with the help of a Smoker's Anonymous club in your town and/or ''How to Quit Smoking" books.

38. *Tailbone Cyst*

Defect in the skin, known as pilonidal sinus, at base of spinal column, varying from a dent to a cluster of tiny sponge-like holes.	Congenital, but usually gives no trouble until late or post-adolescence. Cyst, then, becomes inflamed and painful.	Surgery called for. While not malignant, which some fear, the cyst calls for expert surgery because condition reappears unless all affected tissue is cut away.

39. *Deafness*[1][2]

A condition marked by a partial or total lack in the sense of hearing.	Condition is due either to an obstruction (wax, a boil, ear drum puncture) or a spongy overgrowth called ostoscler-	A specialist can clear up infection and remove conducting interrupters or recommend a hearing aid to aid in bone

Symptom or Problem   **Cause or What It Means**   **What to do**

osis which blocks the transmission of sound to the receiving mechanism. Or it can come from a fault or problem within the skull itself.

conduction. (For a report about hearing aids, write to Consumers Union of the United States, Inc., 256 Washington St., Mount Vernon, N.Y., and pay for one year of reports in return for hearing aid information.) Deafness due to a faulty receiving mechanism in the inner ear or brain which can only be diagnosed by a doctor cannot be helped by hearing aids. Lip reading is helpful, however, and is available through most adult education classes. Call your nearest Community Center college or Visiting Nurse Association.

40. *Diabetes*[13]

A disease that impairs the ability of the body to use sugar and makes for an abnormal amount of sugar in the blood and the urine.

Particularly prevalent in overweight men and women in the 40 to 60 age bracket. (Characteristic: the pancreas does not produce enough insulin to control sugar in the blood, and blood sugar becomes excessive.)

No cure, but careful attention to a diet low in starches, Oral Hypoglycemics, U.S.P., such as Tolbutamide, to stimulate an underactive pancreas and, in severe cases, insulin, can prolong life. Because diabetes is chronic and therapy will go on for life, investigating with your doctor of the least expensive medicines to get desired effect is just plain common sense.

Symptom or Problem	Cause or What It Means	What to do
41. *Diarrhea*		
Intestinal disorder characterized by abnormal frequency and fluidity of fecal evacuations.	Can be symptom of anything from "tourist trots" to ulcerative colitis. If onset is sudden (while on vacation, perhaps) and is accompanied by abdominal pain, headache and nausea, you probably have been infected by a virus as the result of drinking contaminated water or eating unhygienic food. Usually a combination of kaolin and pectin is recommended.	Switch to a liquid diet (i.e., ginger ale and orangeade) to offset loss of liquid. Gradually add Jello, clear soup, toast and other solids. You will recover in 48 hours unless you have more than a "bug," in which case other symptoms plus diarrhea will be present, all of which you can report to a doctor. Call the American Hospital in a foreign country or get the name of a doctor through the American Embassy.
42. *Disfigured Face or other body part*	Unsightly marks or deformities caused by birth defect, an accident or a war injury. Need not cause lifetime embarrassment. What cover-up cosmetics won't hide, plastic surgery and/or artificial parts can take care of.	Buy the best cover-up cosmetic you can find; but after first time, mix your own creams with liquid make-up and rouge from an inexpensive counter. (Such cosmetics have the same ingredients, usually as the more expensive brands; what you pay for is the merchandising.) If your problem is more than skin deep, see a plastic surgeon. As a veteran, you are entitled to free repair; as a civilian, ask your local clinic for the name of a top plastic surgeon. If you do not have insur

Symptom or Problem	Cause or What It Means	What to do
		ance for an expensive repair job, talk to your doctor about finances. Most charge according to "ability to pay."
43. *Slipped Disc*		
Disc of cartilage, which serves as a "cushion" between layers of bone in the spine, some- times slip out of place, causing great discomfort and dif- ficulty in moving.	When a disc slips out from between the bones, it presses on the nerve roots emerging from the spinal cord, thus causing back and leg pain and weakness.	This problem is best handled by a doctor with referral to a neu- rologist and close fol- lowup.
44. *Tic Douloureux*		
Facial neuralgia characterized by paroxysms of pain "triggered" by movement.	Not a neurotic condi- tion, but cause is un- known. Waves of pain may come unexpect- edly, and the slightest jar or chewing will cause eye to water and excruciating pain.	This is a serious disease, mortality 10–15%, and should be handled in a hospital. There is a new U.S.P. drug for this pain called Carbamaze- pine (brand name, Teg- retol) which your doc- tor can tell you about, and also Diphenyl- hydantoin, U.S.P., is helpful. Seek a neurolo- gist's aid.
45. *D.T.'s—Rams*		
(Delirium tremens) A violent restless- ness due to over- imbibing in alcohol, characterized by terror, halucina- tions, trembling, etc.	This acute condition usually comes as the re- sult of a long drinking bout or when an habit- ual drinker is suddenly deprived of alcohol. "Withdrawal sym- ptoms" may be severe enough to require hos- pitalization until the	Should someone in your home be afflicted, call Alcoholics Anony- mous information, an Alcoholism Center or an Alcoholism Care or Family Service office listed in your telephone book. The person who answers will tell you

Symptom or Problem	Cause or What It Means	What to do
	patient becomes secure enough in his mind to function (usually with the help of a doctor) outside of a controlled environment.	what to do and will probably send someone to help. While waiting, give coffee. Reassurance can prevent the patient from injuring himself.

46. *Dowager's Hump*

Characterized by a bent back, middle of chest area, and there may be pain. Later, pain may go but back may become a stiff "poker back."	Usually, the result of years of poor posture. "A young girl's slump means a dowager's hump" still holds true.	When an older woman decides "to straighten up" for cosmetic reasons, she has a difficult time because of habit and arthritic involvement. However, stoop can be arrested by swimming, exercise and change of posture during daily activities (typing, driving, cleaning) that probably made poor posture habitual.

47. *Dysentery*

Infectious disease marked by inflammation of the lower bowel and diarrhea with mucous and hemorrhaging.	Spread by ameba parasite or bacteria in contaminated food and by flies. Headache, flatulence, fever, bowel irregularity and fatigue may be symptoms along with diarrhea.	Even with maximum sanitation in your home, you can wake up with dysentery as the result of having been served contaminated food in a restaurant. Even if your symptoms are mild, consult a doctor who will examine your stool. If ameba parasites are present, Diodoquine plus Terramycin will probably be prescribed. An adult can be an amebic or

Symptom or Problem   **Cause or What It Means**   **What to do**

bacterial "carrier" and can pass dysentery to a child who may become severely ill.

48. *Eczema*

Skin inflammation that causes itching and exudes a serum matter. Both dry and "weeping" eczema can have either an external or internal cause.

Eczema can be caused by an allergy to paint, varnish, photographic material or some other work product. Or it can come from a cosmetic or may be related to hay fever. It sometimes comes along with an emotional upset or as a partner to gout, pregnancy or diabetes.

Try to track down an allergen if eczema comes on suddenly and you have suffered no emotional upset. To relieve local problem, avoid soap and water and cleanse with continuous soaks. Apply calamine lotion if itching is severe. Antihistamines can bring relief in hay fever sufferer.

49. *Emphysema*[14]

Due to inelasticity of lining of the lungs, exhaling is difficult, and lungs remain abnormally inflated.

A large percentage of emphysema sufferers have been heavy smokers. Others have a history of bronchitis and/or asthma.

Stop smoking and, if possible, change to a less harassed way of life in a mild climate. You can prevent mild emphysema from becoming severe or bringing on bronchial problem.

50. *Acquired Epilepsy*

Disorder of the nervous system resulting in loss of consciousness during which time body goes through convulsive movements.

Acquired epilepsy may come as a secondary problem following a tumor, a head injury, an infection, etc.

Investigation should be carried out to find the underlying cause which can then be dealt with. The seizures can be handled symptomatically by use of Diphenylhydantoin or Phenobarbital, U.S.P.

Symptom or Problem	Cause or What It Means	What to do
51. *Common Eye Problem*		
Spots before the eyes which stay in the same relative position to what is being viewed but cannot be brought into focus.	Minute particles are always in the fluid in the globe of the eye; are noticeable when individual is tired, worried or depressed.	Ophthalmologist may recommend change in glasses. In addition, build up general health. Condition will disappear as general health and well-being improves.
52. *Loss of Eyesight*		
Fading eyesight may be due to alcoholism, opaque growth over seeing part of eye, cataracts, diabetes, hemorrhage due to high blood pressure, conjunctivitis, inflammation of transparent window in front of pupil, glaucoma, hardening of the lens.	Cause may be due to malnutrition, aging or a particular disease.	Go to an eye doctor for correct diagnosis. Then, do as advised: quit drinking, have surgery, build up vitality or avoid strain. Should blindness be unavoidable, learn braille so that you can continue to play cards, read, socialize. (See page 207 for where to write for free courses in Braille.)
53. *Tendency to Fall*		
Nearly three times as many people die from falls each year than from burns or drowning or any other accident, not on the highway. More women than men die from falls, and the elderly fall more often than the young.	Faulty eyesight, poor coordination, ill-fitting shoes and carelessness are reasons.	Go through your home carefully, looking for the danger spots. Have rail put along stairway, put mats under loose rugs, have well-lighted landings.

Symptom or Problem	Cause or What It Means	What to do

54. *Flu (Influenza)*

An epidemic disease, caused by a virus, characterized by nasal catarrh, bronchial trouble, general prostration. More common in winter than in summer.

Announces itself with fever, achy feeling, nausea, chills, cold symptoms. Not to be taken lightly; can be forerunner of pneumonia.

Go to bed, and stay there until all symptoms go. Stay away from others in family. Work to avoid flu by taking vaccine if you are especially vulnerable (i.e., pregnant, elderly or have a chronic disease), avoiding crowds, building up resistance with good food, adequate exercise, rest.

55. *Food Poisoning*

Caused by toxin that forms in spoiled food, contaminated or canned goods, or by germs from hands of baker in baked goods, or by bacteria or from fish from polluted environment or from poison plants like inedible mushrooms.

Vomiting and diarrhea coming on shortly after eating is nature's way of getting rid of poison.

Vomit what you can and drink clear liquids —ginger ale, tea—to compensate for lost liquid. Trouble usually leaves in a few hours and is seldom more than a temporary distress.

56. *Foot Trouble*

Seven out of ten adults have foot problems, and overweight and poor-fitting shoes are the principal causes. (Overweight contributes to flat and/or tired feet;

Athlete's Foot is caused by a fungus which thrives on warm, moist skin; warts and corns on the soles of the feet are often caused by infection; anyone with poor circulation (especially those with diabe-

Deep-seated corns, calluses and bunions should be removed and/or treated by a chiropodist or podiatrist. To remove a simple corn, soak feet in warm water, apply a few drops of salicylic acid

Symptom or Problem	Cause or What It Means	What to do
poor-fitting shoes make for corns, calluses, bunions and ingrown toenails.)	tes) should take special care of feet to avoid gangrene.	in 10 percent solution of collodion, soak feet again. Corn will lift off. To clear up athlete's foot, apply Zinc Undecylenate, U.S.P., (Desenex) as directed. For tired feet, give alternating baths of hot and cold water, wear comfortable shoes, relax before sleeping with feet propped higher than head.

57. *Gall Bladder Trouble*[15]

Any malfunction of the little pouch under the right lobe of the liver in which bile is stored which assists in the digestion of fats. Pain on right side below ribs or up by right shoulder blade comes as a first sign.	Most trouble (inflammation, biliary, colic, etc.) is due to presence or passage of gallstones (consisting of fatty cholesterol) or by stones or scarred bladder. Acute problems come usually after eating fatty foods.	Restrict fatty foods. Lose weight. Have gall bladder removed if necessary.

58. *Glaucoma*

Increased pressure in the eye with progressive loss of vision. Most prevalent in persons over 40 and tends to run in families.	Colored rings and halos at edge of range of vision may be warning sign, but often there is little to announce glaucoma except for gradual loss of seeing power, scarcely noticeable in the beginning. For this reason, regular tests for	No home treatment known, but eye doctor can do much for glaucoma if discovered early. Adults over 50 (especially women) should have eye examination every 18 months. Usual fee by ophthalmologist: $15

Symptom or Problem	Cause or What It Means	What to do
	faulty fluid flow are advised.	to $25, but during public health drives, examinations are given free by public health doctors in temporary quarters. (Eye drops containing the new drug, protyptiline, sometimes combined with norepinephrine, have been found to control deterioration. Use by eye doctors is not general as yet, but research is being done and progress is reported.)

59. *Gout*

Constitutional disease more common to men than to women, characterized by painful inflammation of joints of feet and hands and excess uric acid in the blood and urine.	Wine, beer, high protein diet, rich food, can aggravate tendency to gout, which is a painful and disabling disease. Severe gout can bring permanent damage to joints and kidneys.	Lose weight, change to simple diet of cheese, fruit, vegetables, fish and drink 10 to 12 glasses of water, fruit juice or weak tea or coffee per day. To relieve severe pain, take aspirin, and to cut down excess uric acid, take Colchicine.

60. *Gray Hair*

Color faded from hair due to loss of pigments in hair.	Air spaces in individual hairs become exaggerated during aging process. This combined with pigment loss makes for graying and whitening.	No way to stop color loss, which progresses according to hereditary make-up and in a few isolated cases is speeded up by worry. Only way to restore hair color is to apply it.

61. *Hangover*

Disagreeable effects of drunkenness,	Alcohol dilates blood vessels in the skull,	For a giant hangover, stay in bed, if possible,

Symptom or Problem	Cause or What It Means	What to do
usually experienced ''the morning after.''	causing tension-type headache; effects nervous system, causing shakiness, numbness and "blackouts." Morning-after "guilt" often creates psychological discomfort, too. Combination of ills makes for real distress.	take aspirin, caffeine tablet and vitamins. Drink a lot of fluids. Eat soft, soothing food (milk toast, cooked cereal, toast and hot tea). Next time, be more careful about spacing drinks. Eat food, too, if tolerable.

62. *Hay Fever*

Catarrhal condition of the mucous membranes of eyes and respiratory tract which affects persons susceptible to certain plant pollens.	Seasonal hay fever comes annually when specific pollens are in the air; perennial hay fever, due to dust, cat hair, etc., can come anytime. Inflammation of eyes, ears, nose and bronchial tubes may be secondary and even more serious problems.	Go away from home during hay fever season, if possible; get rid of animal causing problem and sleep in dust-free, air-conditioned room. But the real boon is the antihistamine treatment. Chlorpheniramine Maleate, U.S.P., is especially potent as is Tripelennamine Hydrochloride, U.S.P. Some experimenting may be necessary to find what particular remedy gives relief without nausea.

63. *Migraine Headache*[16]

Severe pounding headache in one side of head, nausea. May upset vision.	Such vascular headaches do not have a definite known cause.	One specific prescription is available: Ergotamine Tartrate, U.S.P., plus caffeine.

64. *Tension Headache*[16]

Caused by tightened muscles in the neck and scalp.	Comes as the result of long hours over typewriter or books, worry,	Take a hot shower or lie in warm tub with back of neck below

Symptom or Problem	Cause or What It Means	What to do
Usually starts at the base of skull, encircles head.	emotional tension.	water level. Take aspirin, eat lightly and do your best to relax. If headaches are habitual, talk to both a doctor and a psychiatrist to find out the cause. In time of overwork, massage can help to circumvent headache.

65. *Heartburn*

Uneasy burning sensation in the stomach, extending toward esophagus, sometimes accompanied by spitting up of acid fluid.	Heartburn has nothing to do with the heart; comes as a result of sluggish stomach and duodenum. (Pregnant women especially susceptible.)	If frequently bothered, go easy on gas-forming and rich foods, try to exercise more and take a teaspoon of milk of magnesia or Maalox when you feel particularly upset internally.

66. *Heart Disorders*[17]

Any malfunction of the hollow muscular organ, which by rhythmic relaxations and contractions keeps the blood in circulation throughout the body.	Characterized by heart beat which differs from normal rhythm of 60 to 80 beats per minute. Beat may be fluttering, rapid (or in rare instances, slow) or there may be heart failure or a disorder of the valves or trouble in the coronary arteries. Symptoms: fast or slow pulse, combined usually with one of the following—swelling of the feet and ankles, breathlessness, fever, headaches, dizziness, cough, blueness, cold hands and feet. In an acute	Change may come along with or as an aftermath of fever, anemia, jaundice, diabetes, or rheumatic fever, a kidney disorder, or it may result from strain from high blood pressure or from an emotional upset or extreme nervousness. Any heart disorder should be looked into by a doctor, and proper medicine to relieve the basic cause and heart involvement will be prescribed. Above all, a good mental outlook should be encouraged in the

Symptom or Problem	Cause or What It Means	What to do
	case, there will be collapse.	patient by his or her family. A heart disorder does not have to mean death.

67. *Hemorrhoids*

A swelling of the veins under the mucous membrane or skin inside or just outside the rectum. Result may be loss of blood, pain, rectal fissures, anemia.	One of the most common ailments of mankind, hemorrhoids may come from straining due to constipation or from pressure during pregnancy or a tumor in the abdomen or from a heart or liver disorder or from high blood pressure or cancer.	To relieve pain, take warm sit-down baths. Use suppository to soften stool; retain until it can be passed without a problem. When in severe pain, use Dibucaine, U.S.P., as a local anesthetic applied as ointment. In emergency, ask your pharmacist to call your doctor for a verbal prescription to give relief until you can get to the office. If persistent, go for examination to find basic cause.

68. *Hepatitis*

Inflammation of the liver due to a virus transmitted in contaminated food or water by a needle previously used on hepatitis sufferer.	Characterized by jaundice and whitish stool due to bile in blood stream and absence of bile in bowels. May be accompanied by fatigue, a tired feeling, anemia or hemorrhoids; rarely can lead to cirrhosis of the liver.	Bed rest, abstinence from alcohol and good diet.

69. *Hernia*

Protrusion of an organ or tissue through an opening in its surrounding wall.	Usually appearing in the groin of a male or female (inguinal), the upper thigh of a female (femoral), or in the	Therapy depends on the type of hernia. Inguinal and femoral require surgery. Umbilical does not and usu-

Symptom or Problem	Cause or What It Means	What to do
	navel of the infant (umbilical).	ally closes by the age of two. If the lump cannot be pushed back, whatever the type, the circulation is cut off causing strangulation. Do not wait for a doctor; if this happens, get to the hospital. Gangrene can set in and death can come within six hours.

70. *Congenital Dislocated Hip*

A congenital condition, more common to girls than boys, which makes for a peculiar gait or limp. If not cared for in infancy, this makes for a serious problem later on. This condition can be diagnosed in infancy by careful physical examination by a doctor: extra skinfold on side of dislocation and difficulty in putting baby in frog's leg position.	Poorly formed socket and loose ligament so that bone is displaced from its socket. Dislocation may produce pain or locking in hip (or in shoulder, knee, finger, toe or any other joint).	Position of frog leg is maintained by extra diaper or special cast. Operation may be necessary to reduce and fix thigh bone in hip joint. If neglected, faulty hip joint can lead to arthritis.

71. *Fractured Hip*

A common accident for elderly women.	Actually, "broken hip" is a fracture of the neck of the thigh bone, usually resulting from a fall. Foot turns out; hip area is painful; bruising present.	Go for X-ray. If hip is broken, an orthopedic expert will probably recommend surgery followed by rest.

Symptom or Problem	Cause or What It Means	What to do
72. *Hoarseness*		
Harsh, weak and/or breathy manner of speaking.	Caused by chronic laryngitis due to smoking, overuse of alcohol, sinus trouble, abused vocal cords or swelling of the larynx due to infection. Occasionally, a cancer on the vocal cord may be causing problem. Because of this, get to throat specialist for X-ray if you are hoarse for longer than a week or two.	If no physical basis is found for hoarseness, stop smoking and go to nearby university for speech therapy. If you have a catarrhal infection, take antihistamines for relief.
73. *Hysterectomy*		
Removal of the uterus through surgery.	Recommended when fibroid tumors (usually benign) form in the uterus, causing menstrual problems, backache, constipation, urinary distress. Also recommended when scraping of uterus shows cancer.	Ovaries are not removed. Thus, sexual enjoyment is not lessened; childbearing, however, is over. In case of cancer, a hysterectomy is usually followed by X-ray treatments.
74. *Indigestion*[18]		
Impairment of the ability to digest food.	Food is digested in the stomach and intestines with the help of natural juices and enzymes manufactured there. Disruption of the normal digestive process can be caused by nervousness, over-indulgence in rich foods and/or alcohol, gall bladder trouble, appen-	For a mild acid indigestion, take ½ tsp. of soda in ½ glass of water or fruit juice and feel a "burp" of relief. For a more disturbing upset, take Maalox or Aluminum Hydroxide Gel. Make an effort to slow down your eating (and your life!) and relax with wine before or

Symptom or Problem	Cause or What It Means	What to do
	dicitis, a "bug," or an ulcer or cancer. Obviously, constant digestive trouble should be analyzed by a doctor.	during your meals. If you suspect nervousness, take a mild tranquilizer or antihistamine to encourage drowsiness at bedtime. Go easy in all departments of your life.

75. *Insomnia*

Sleeplessness for a long period, night after night.	Usual causes are: (1) too wound up to sleep; (2) a physical problem like bladder trouble that makes for frequent urinating, heart trouble which makes night breathing a problem, arthritis which is painful; (3) an emotional problem that makes for sleep disturbances.	(1) Do not eat a heavy meal just before bedtime. (2) Get physically tired by some vigorous physical activity during the day. (3) Take hot milk with rum or whiskey followed by a hot bath. (4) Go to bed one half hour earlier than you want to get to sleep. Once in bed, read or watch TV or write a letter to someone who is fond of you and postpone thinking about sleep. (5) Take an aspirin to relieve headache if that keeps you awake. (6) Take a mild sedative if you have to get up early and *must* have sleep.

76. *Painful Intercourse*

Discomfort of either a man or woman during sexual relations.	Can be caused by overweight of man; lack of lubrication of woman's vagina; tightening of muscles of vagina entrance due to fear of childbirth; psychologi-	Change position, lying on side, face to face, for instance, during wife's pregnancy or when man is overweight. Discuss any psychological problem

Symptom or Problem	Cause or What It Means	What to do
	cal fear of harming pregnant woman's unborn child; non-stiff penis and man's embarrassment about same; an actual injury (stitches in woman from childbirth, recent hysterectomy, local infection, hernia in man).	with a therapist (not a marriage counselor unless he's a psychologist, too). Consult doctor about true physical problem. Talk problem over with your mate, working together to make intercourse more enjoyable.
77. *Jaundice*		
Condition comes from bile pigments in blood; characterized by yellowness of skin and whites of eyes, lassitude and loss of appetite.	A symptom rather than a disease in itself. Signifies trouble with gall bladder or liver.	Treat basic cause (surgery, ususally, for gall bladder stones interfering with bile current; rest, bland diet and abstinence from alcohol for hepatitis).
78. *Kidney Problems*[19]		
Disturbance in one or both of the bean-shaped organs at the back of the abdominal cavity which excrete urine.	Most common problems: (1) kidney stones, caused from solidifying salts in the urine which block urine from going through ureter to bladder; (2) infection secondary to obstruction; (3) infection from teeth, tonsils, etc., passed through blood to kidneys; (4) abscess or tumor; (5) nephritis due to allergy to streptococus. Pain in side, fever, headache, cloudy or bloody urine are characteristics.	Usual remedies: Plenty of liquids (four or five quarts a day), sulfa for infection, special diet if stones are present; surgery if stones do not pass or if tumor is present. Rare: graft of new kidneys, if kidneys fail in their function.
79. *Laryngitis*		
Inflammation of the muscle and car-	Usually comes with cold or throat infection	Steam inhalations give local relief as do most

Symptom or Problem	Cause or What It Means	What to do
tilage structure in the upper part of the windpipe where vocal cords are located.	and affects the voice.	of the remedies listed under Hoarseness. Post nasal drip aggravates problem so antihistimines relieve, if sinus problem is allergy-caused. Laryngitis associated with cold usually disappears with it.

80. *Leprosy*

A chronic disease characterized by numbness and lesions or nodules infected with leprae bacteria.	Families of boys in southeast Asia fear that leprosy can be caught from a leper on the street. Not true. While leprosy is infectious, it is not overly contagious, and can be arrested.	Your doctor will help you get into National Sanitarium for Leprosy at Carville, Louisiana. Care is free and an arrest of the disease is pretty much assured.

81. *Leukorrea*

Whitish discharge from the female genital organs.	Sexual excitement, gonorrhea, syphilis, polyps, cancer, inflammation of cervix, lack of acid balance, bacterial infection, old age, allergies.	Take mild vinegar and warm water douche for several days straight. If discharge doesn't clear up, consult doctor who will help you find basic cause. Do not expect him to moralize. He's a physician, not a minister.

82. *Cirrhosis of the Liver*

Hardening of the liver, causing pollution of blood stream by bile plus a backing up of blood into veins, causing serious	Associated with alcoholism, but due to nutritional deficiency, infection and gall bladder problems as much as to over-drinking. Symptoms: jaundice, fatigue,	Hardening comes when damaged cells fail to replace themselves. Remaining cells *must* be preserved to maintain life. Should you suspect liver trouble, get to a

Symptom or Problem	Cause or What It Means	What to do
complications.	anemia, swollen abdomen and ankles, hemorrhaging veins, black stools, nausea.	doctor who will recommend bed rest, nutritious vitamin-rich diet and total abstinence. With proper care, you can live happily with only 20% of live cells.

83. *Lockjaw*

A spasm of the muscles of mastication due to infection caused by tetanus bacteria in the soil which enters body through skin puncture.	Between one and two weeks after injury, lockjaw occurs along with pain in the back of the neck and fever. Wound may or may not look infected.	If you have not had anti-tetanus immunization, go for injection when injury takes place. Even if you have had shot, have booster shot.

84. *Lumbago*

Low back pain and/or shooting pains in groin.	May come from strain of muscles, long cramped position while traveling or standing, or a true back injury (slipped disc, arthritis, poor posture).	For pain due to strain, go to bed, take aspirin and have a massage, if possible. For chronic lumbago, search out deeper problem and treat accordingly.

85. *Meniere's Disease*[20]

Disturbance of the balancing mechanism in the inner ear.	Comes in middle age, more common to men than women. Symptoms: dizziness, nausea, deafness or ringing in one ear.	Go to ear specialist who will give Dimenhydrinate, U.S.P., for antinausea and for stabilizing effect. Attacks may recur for years, but deafness can be prevented with medicinal help, and disease eventually runs itself out.

86. *Menopausal Difficulties*

The average woman's monthly	Hot flashes, perspiration, cold extremities,	If you are troubled, (1) ask your doctor to pre-

Symptom or Problem **Cause or What It Means** **What to do**

cycle of ovulation and menstruation ceases when she is between 45 and 50. Because of the non-production of hormones her body had become accustomed to, her endocrine system is temporarily disturbed and some emotional and physical symptoms may cause concern. "Going through the menopause" usually takes about three years, during which time the menses become scanty and eventually cease.

headache, irritability and inability to breathe may be symptoms. Unfounded beliefs that menopause can mean a loss of feminity and/or judgment or even the mind can aggravate physical symptoms and vice versa. Also, because the nest empties about this time, a woman can tell herself that "life is over" now that the children are gone.

scribe estrogen tablets which provide the female hormones your body no longer produces, and (2) talk to a certified psychologist or psychiatrist. For the name of a certified analyst and/or gynecologist, call your county medical association. Should there be bleeding after menstruation has supposedly stopped, go to gynecologist immediately.

87. Mental Problems

The person who has unreasonable fears, is extremely agitated or anxious, loses contact with the world around him, has no insight into his own behavior or is an extreme hypochondriac, is mentally ill from a physical problem (syphilis, brain tumor or infection) or has a functional brain disorder such as schizophrenia, or

Because of toxic psychosis due to drug or alcohol addiction, a physical problem or a psychopathic problem caused or aggravated by a stress situation at home, an individual may lose contact with reality. When this happens, he should have the care of mental health experts.

If you are extremely agitated, worried or despondent (or if another in your family is in this state), go to a nearby psychiatric clinic and talk through your problem. This is the first step in a sound mental health program, which may include hospitalization, psychotherapy, group therapy, drugs, shock treatment and other enlightened remedies. When seeking help on your own, go

Symptom or Problem	Cause or What It Means	What to do
a psychosomatic disease.	ponent as much as from an allergy and/or bacterial mechanism.	withstand the tension produced by this never-ending problem. Also, if the emotional tension is aggravated and/or inner-produced, therapy may be indicated.

94. Neuroses and Psychoses

Emotional disorders in which anxieties, compulsions and physical complaints (with no basis in disease) dominate the personality. (While a psychosis is more severe than a neurosis, both are conditions in which the total personality suffers.)	Usually, an upset childhood is the basis for a neurotic problem in later life. The same may be true of the psychotic individual, but there is sometimes an actual brain damage, too, resulting from infection, disease, drugs, senility, neglect in childhood, or an accident. There is no doubt, however, that many years of neglect and abuse take their toll.	Go to your nearest mental health clinic for advice about where to go to find help with your neurotic phobias or compulsions. Or to discuss what to do about someone in your family suffering from a true psychosis. (This is the difference between a neurotic and a psychotic: the neurotic, while unhappy because of anxiety, fears and symptoms has a firm grasp on reality; the psychotic individual has lost his grip on reality and believes what he imagines to be true.)

95. Neuritis[22]

Inflammation of a nerve, usually producing pain, often accompanied by a sensory disturbance.	Peripheral nerves, containing both pain and motor fibers, become inflamed as a result of a vitamin deficiency, alcoholism, an allergy, diabetes, a bacterial infection.	For general neuritis, once the cause is known, treatment is usually general. A good diet, extra vitamins, especially B, plenty of rest, lack of tension, physiotherapy and a go

Symptom or Problem	Cause or What It Means	What to do
		at the cause (i.e., no alcohol for alcoholics), control of diabetes, elimination of toxins.
96. *Numbness*		
Usually a condition of the extremities, in which a hand or foot or leg is deprived of sensation.	Can be a result of heart trouble, anemia, high blood pressure, alcoholism, disturbance of nerves in arteries, drugs, multiple sclerosis, neuritis or some other physical problem.	Think through your daily life. Are you over-drinking, emotionally upset, tense? If not, and if the upset has come on suddenly, report this symptom and others to a neurologist, who will find and treat the cause.
97. *Obesity*		
Excessively fat, overweight for size and age. Not a disease in itself but a disease-maker, contributing to heart and kidney problems, diabetes, foot trouble and dozens of other disabilities.	It is rare that disease or glands or that menopause or heredity is the cause in itself of overweight. (Kidney trouble and heart trouble make for puffiness, but that is not true fat.) And though fat runs in families, it is usually due to overeating rather than to body type. Most people who are overweight get that way by overeating meal after meal, and between meals, too.	Diet—but do it sensibly—possibly with the help of a group of adults in your same boat. Call Weight Watchers, TOPS and/or other reducing clubs and do as the others do. Forget get-thin-fast diets; you'll take the weight off, but you'll put it on again. What you have to do is to change your eating habits for life. Join a group.
98. *Malfunction of the Pancreas* [23]		
Any condition due to non-functioning of the pancreas, a long, fish-shaped	Most common result of a malfunctioning pancreas is diabetes, caused by the non-digestion of	Diabetes usually occurs in overweight people who eat an abundance of starches and sugar.

Symptom or Problem   **Cause or What It Means**   **What to do**

gland behind the stomach. (Made of two different tissues, the cells in one of which secrete pancreatic juice for food digestion; in the other, insulin, which the body must have to use sugar.)

sugar. Because the main part of the pancreas produces juices which help to digest proteins and fats, any disruption there results in an inability to assimilate protein for necessary body repair.

Whether diabetes is an inherited tendency or the pancreas is unable to do its job because of the overload is questionable. Anyway, the necessity for cutting down on weight is obvious for the diabetic, as is the need to lower sugar and starch intake. As far as the other function of the pancreas, there is a need to cut down on fat when there is trouble there.

99. *Paralysis*

Loss or impairment of movement due to injury or disease of nerves, brain or spinal cord.

Damage to nerves makes for the inability to use a body part. If the damage is in the brain or spinal cord, various muscle groups will be weak, but there will be no atrophy. There may be a great deal of function to be regained. If the nerve cells or peripheral nerves are injured, then, the muscles become atrophied as in polio or with a severed nerve. Occasionally, hysteria produces paralysis.

Rehabilitation of a paralyzed muscle consists of mending the severed nerve, removing a tumor pressing on a nerve. Physiotherapy then can be employed to maintain function until healing process is complete. Paralysis due to hysteria is a psychological problem, calls for a psychiatrist as well as a neurologist.

100. *Parkinson's Disease*
(Shaking Palsy)

A nerve disease due to abnormality in

Follows encephalitis, hardening of the

Keep mind active, hopefully doing

Symptom or Problem	Cause or What It Means	What to do
brain, characterized by tremors of fingers and hands, mask-like face, difficulty with initiating movement and rigidity of body.	arteries. Thinking process is not affected, just muscular control of the body.	creative work which will boost spirits even though muscles deteriorate. New medicine L-Dopa is available which has been approved by U.S. Food and Drug Administration. Neurosurgery is also of value.

101. *Pediculosis*

Infected with lice—head lice, body lice and crab lice, which inhabit sex area.	Itching, due to biting of parasites which live on host's blood, and scratching, which can lead to small infected sores. Lice are dirty gray.	DDT and benzyl benzoate are effective against head and body lice. Kwell ointment gets rid of pubic lice.

102. *Pleurisy*[24]

Inflammation of delicate membrane which lines chest cavity and covers lungs. Can be either dry or wet.	After pneumonia, bronchitis, or a cold, dry pleurisy brings severe pain due to inflamed places rubbing against each other, makes for cough and fever. Wet pleurisy brings pain at first, which subsides leaving patient with feeling of debilitation and breathlessness.	Find from X-ray whether there is tubercular involvement. If infection is nontubercular but severe, take Penicillin G, (and/or other penicillin as prescribed by your doctor). After infection subsides, abdominal breathing is a help.[25] Hot baths or heating pad will ease pain.

103. *Pneumonia*

Bacterial infection of the lungs due to pneumococcus, staphylococcus, other bacteria or a virus infection.	Because inflammation gets into air sacs in lungs, breathing becomes rapid to make up for lost capacity. At onset, temperature goes	Pneumococcus and/or staphylococcus can usually be checked by Penicillin G before disease becomes deadly. If virus infection is pre-

Symptom or Problem	Cause or What It Means	What to do
	up, there is chest pain and breathlessness plus cough with mucous and/or blood.	sent, no antibiotic is prescribed. Inhalations will loosen sputum when there is bronchial involvement, heat will relieve pain, propped-up position will aid breathing.

104. *Pregnancy Complications*[26]

Pregnancy: Women may be "on edge" emotionally during pregnancy, become overweight, look "puffy," feel nauseated, vomit, be troubled with indigestion, hemorrhoids, varicose veins, swelling of ankles, shortness of breath and backache.	Due to readjustments in body chemistry from hormone changes, a pregnant woman may be unusually fretful or "hyped up." And because of new anxieties, she may overeat and become overweight. This may cause foot and leg troubles and inner physical pressures, resulting in constipation, hemorrhoids, backache, etc.	Keep your weight down; give up smoking to ease circulatory problems; eat plenty of natural "laxative" foods; drink eight glasses of fluid a day to flush kidneys and bladder; cut out salt. Above all, remember this condition is temporary. Two real danger signals: puffiness which can mean toxemia of pregnancy, bleeding, which can mean miscarriage or other problem. Get doctor at once to save your and your baby's life.

105. *Post Nasal Drip*

Dripping behind the nose due to chronic sinusitis (rare) or more common catarrh which is an inflammation of mucous membranes making for in-	Problem may be result of cold, smoker's irritation, infection of teeth or tonsils, allergy.	To ease pain, stay out of cold, dry air and inhale moist hot air from vaporizer. To stop drip, give up smoking, take antihistamine which will be effective if allergy is cause.

Symptom or Problem	Cause or What It Means	What to do

creased secretions of glands.

106. *Prostate Trouble*

Infection, tumor or enlargement from unknown cause of the muscular, glandular organ which surrounds the urethra of males (usually older ones) at base of bladder.	The gland, which creates a fluid which helps to make up semen, may become cancerous in which case burning and frequency of urination plus blood may be sign. Or it may become enlarged at the age 50 or later. Here, the symptoms will also be related to urinating due to the urethra's being pressed by the enlarged gland.	Go for examination if you have a symptom described here. Early diagnosis of cancer can mean arrest; early diagnosis of enlargement can prevent kidney infection. Treatment will be directed to unblocking the bladder through catheterization and/or surgical removal of part of the gland which is not difficult when performed by expert.

107. *Psoriasis*

Common chronic skin disease characterized by scaly silvery patches over reddened spots, located characteristically on scalp, elbows, knees, chest, back and buttocks. There is usually a disturbance of nail growth.	Not infectious; not caused by known allergy; not catching. May be related to lack of sunlight; may have emotional cause. Appears in young adults far more often than in young children or older people.	Dermatologist can be of help here. He will certainly recommend sunbaths in natural sunlight. He may use cortisone or tar ointment. If emotional distress is great, he will recommend a psychiatrist.

108. *Pyorrhea*

Progressive disease of the gums characterized by the formation of pus in pockets between the roots of	First stage: red, swollen gums which bleed easily. Second more severe state comes if first stage is neglected.	Have tartar removed every six months by dentist; brush up and down to get rid of food deposits in pockets; clean daily with floss

Symptom or Problem	Cause or What It Means	What to do
the teeth and their surrounding tissues; frequently accompanied by loosening of the teeth.		and mouthwash; eat large quantities of oranges, tomatoes, grapefruit, etc., for extra Vitamin C (ascorbic acid) necessary for healthy gums.

109. *Quinsy*

Inflammation of the tonsils due to abscess and pus. Neck is swollen.	Severe pain, spreading into neck and ear; difficulty in swallowing; high fever; swelling, usually on one side of throat only, drainage into throat.	Usual recommendation: Aspirin for pain; Penicillin G for infection. Tonsillectomy, if problem is severe and persistent.

110. *Rectal Itching*

Usually due to internal hemorrhoids.	Itching pain in moist skin comes from excess mucous.	If constipation is present, a suppository at night may lubricate stool so that it can be easily passed in morning. If bleeding is present, consult doctor who may perform operation. Use hot Sitz Baths and Nupercainal Ointment.

111. *Rectal Fissure*

A groove or split in rectum wall. Symptom: pain plus streaks of bright, red blood in stool.	Pain may be a dull ache in rectal area, changing to stabbing pain at time of bowel movement. Can be the result of long time strain to pass hard stools. More common to women that to men.	Under doctor's direction, take Dioctyl Sodium Succinafe, N.F., to soften stool. (Do not buy expensive "name" brand; same formula is available at 1/5th the price under other names.) Xylocaine lubricant eases surface pain.

Symptom or Problem   **Cause or What It Means**   **What to do**

112. *Sarcoidosis*

A disease characterized by granular lessions of the skin, lymph nodes, lungs and eyes.

Affects dark skinned persons more often than light. Cause unknown; not catching; can be disabling. (Because it invades lungs, it is sometimes confused with tuberculosis. Not related.)

Fever, weight loss, sometimes a cough. Little lumps in tissues disappear some docotrs have reported, when patient is given cortisone and ACTH.

113. *Sciatica*

Neuralgia of the sciatic nerve, which extends from the hip down the back of the thigh.

Pain starts in back, radiates down leg as the result of pressure on nerves emerging from spinal cord. Common cause of pressures: slipped disc.

Rest on hard bed (with board under mattress) plus aspirin. May need complete X-ray of the spinal column. Conservative therapy may be necessary before operation. If pressure is caused by tumor or pelvic inflammation, doctor's help is needed to get at cause.

114. *Sexual Maladjustment*

Inability to enjoy the sex act with a satisfying orgasm.

There may be physical reasons why erection is impossible for the male, and/or an orgasm is not realized by the female, but once possible abnormalities are checked out and both parties are found to be normal, any unpleasantness has to be due to a psychological cause.

If unconscious tensions in one or both partners prevent satisfaction, a psychologist or psychiatrist can work wonders. First step: the desire on the part of both the man and the woman to build a lasting and enjoyable relationship. With that step accomplished, the rest comes easy.

Symptom or Problem	Cause or What It Means	What to do
115. *Skin Flare-ups*[27]		
Skin problems in an adult can come from an allergy, an emotional upset or an infection.	An allergy may cause hives, a flushing of blood vessels or a drug rash. An emotional upset may aggravate a tendency to acne, eczema and other skin diseases. Skin can also be infected by bacteria, which causes boils, carbuncles, impetigo and other flare-ups.	Antihistamine tablets will relieve hives and other allergy-produced skin upsets. Relief from tension can ease skin problems. And specific topical ointments and lotions can take care of bacterial infections. (Look up specific problem in this book.) Diet, rest, cleanliness and lack of strain are basic requisites of good skin care.
116. *Shingles (Herpes Zoster)*		
Disease affecting roots of peripheral nerves, causing blisters and rash on skin along path of nerve. Thought by some to be related to chicken pox virus—affecting adults as shingles, children as pox.	Caused by virus; brings blisters, itching, discomfort. Once believed to cause death if complete circling of body took place, known now not to be true. If facial nerve affected, shingles can affect eyes, causing scarring.	Usual recommendation by doctor or clinic: For relief from pain, take aspirin or stronger analgesic and apply a topical antibiotic to reduce itching and for the prevention of a secondary infection. Virus wears itself out in about two weeks.
117. *Frozen Shoulder*		
Stiffness and pain in joint eventually causing immobility.	Usually affects middle-aged women who are not particularly active. They first notice tenderness, then sense deeper discomfort in shoulder.	Heat, exercise and swimming may be helpful. Also, massage and manipulation (possibly under an anesthetic). To prevent freezing, joint must be kept mobile.

Symptom or Problem   **Cause or What It Means**   **What to do**

118. *Chronic Sinusitis*

Unceasing inflammation of the sinuses (rare). Problem usually comes and goes in attacks of two-week duration.

Symptoms: Blocked nostril; bad breath; headache; occasional ear involvement. Also, throat involvement, which makes for soreness and/or hoarseness. Cause may be anything from an allergy to a deformity.

First, look for cause on your own. Take antihistamines and phenylephrine nose drops for one week. Avoid diving which may force water into sinus cavities. Walk briskly in the open air every day, deep-breathing through one nostril and exhaling through the other as you go. If no improvement, go to an ear, nose and throat man for sinus washout and have X-ray to search out deformity.

119. *Sleeping Sickness*

Two types: one rare in the United States, is caused by protozoan, carried by tsetse fly; the second, known here, is a virus disease called encephalitis. Both make for extreme muscular weakness, apathy and/ or coma.

Encephalitis, sometimes called brain fever, can leave brain damage or may be fatal but more often there is complete recovery.

Get to a neurologist and do exactly what he says. Probably, he will isolate patient in hospital until fever goes, and patient is over acute disease. Physiotherapy will be recommended during acute and chronic parts of disease.

120. *Sore Throat*[28]

Characterized by one or more of the following: pain, swollen glands, referred pain in ear, difficulting in

May be local infection due to streptococcus or other germ, or may be first symptom of a cold or other illness.

Take aspirin to relieve pain, antihistamine to counteract allergic manifestations of colds. Throat can be cultured to determine if cause is

Symptom or Problem	Cause or What It Means	What to do
swallowing, tickling or raspy feeling in throat.		"strep." However, doctor may feel from looking at throat that he knows cause is bacterial and so will prescribe penicillin. Whatever the cause, curtail activity, drink liquids to make up for loss of liquid through running nose and/or increased perspiration. Watch for other symptoms giving clue to basic problem.

121. *Stroke*

A sudden attack of focal neurologic deficit usually manifested by paralysis of a body part due to bleeding in the brain or a clot in an artery which supplies brain tissue. Hypertension and arteriosclerosis are basic causes.	While only 15 percent of persons with high blood pressure eventually have a stroke, hypertension is the leading cause of intracerebral bleeds. If an artery has been damaged, narrowed or thickened by arteriosclerosis, the blood flow is lessened and a clot may form suddenly. Death results if hemorrhage damages large area of the brain.	Today, clot removal by a brain surgeon, operations on arteries in the neck, blood-thinning through new medicines and rehabilitation by trained therapists can work wonders.

122. *Sunburn*

Inflammation of the skin caused by exposure to rays of the sun or a sun lamp.	Fair, delicate and young skins burn more easily than others, and some disease (tuberculosis, kidney disease) are aggravated by sunburn. In most cases, the burn is superficial or	For superficial burns: stand under cool shower to ease pain, or take cool bath. Drink extra liquids to offset liquids lost in perspiration; take aspirin. For severe burn (with blisters

Symptom or Problem   **Cause or What It Means**   **What to do**

first degree; sometimes, however, blisters result, and the affected person has fever and chills.

and/or chills): call doctor, take cool bath containing soda, pat dry, get to bed, and keep cool, keep feet propped higher than head and take aspirin. Put a sterile dressing (gauze), impregnated with vaseline to prevent sticking over exposed flesh.

123. *Syphilis*

A chronic infectious disease caused by a spirochete, which is usually venereal in origin and only rarely congenital.

Because syphilis is *hidden,* its presence may not be recognized by the carrier. That's why a blood test is given routinely in most states before a marriage license is granted or a pregnant woman delivers her baby, or a man enters the armed forces or a prospective blood donor gives blood. Because syphilis *in the first and second stage* is highly contagious, any abnormality of the genital organs should be reported to the doctor at once. Discovered in time, the disease can be cured quite easily. Left untreated, syphilis can effect the heart, lungs and brain.

Should you become aware of the first sign of syphilis, a hard, non-painful ulcer (usually in the sex area), go to a clinic at once. (Free blood tests are given by the United States Public Health Department in most cities, free, and free shots are given in many clinics. For full details, call your Area Coordinator for the Health, Education and Welfare Department, listed under United States Government. Or your doctor will provide the service for a small fee.) A blood test may not prove positive at this time but a smear under a microscope will show syphilis germs. During the second stage (a little more than two

Symptom or Problem   Cause or What It Means   What to do

months later), a rash
may appear.

In first two stages, the
disease will be highly
contagious. Then, and
until the disease is
cured, the affected per-
son's blood test will be
positive. To effect a
complete cure, today's
doctor gives penicillin
injections for 8 to 12
days.

**124. *Loss of Permanent
Teeth***

Common causes:
decay, pyorrhea.
Other reasons:
accidents, im-
pacted teeth, nec-
essary bite repair,
or a teeth straight-
ening job.

Basic causes of decay:
lack of calcium and
spark-plug Vitamin D
during fast-growing
years, or during preg-
nancy; two many
sweets especially late at
night; poor brushing
habits. Basic causes of
gum problems: lack of
Vitamin C, build-up of
plaque or tartar, food
deposits between teeth
and near gum line.

While cavities become
less prevalent with age,
the wear and tear on
teeth from a lifetime of
use and the result of
malocclusion become
more and more
apparent. Also, pyor-
rhea becomes far of a
problem. Thus, profes-
sional advice and care is
as important as ever.
have a professional
cleaning and checkup
every six months, eat a
balanced diet contain-
ing essential minerals
plus Vitamin D enrich-
ed milk served "as is"
or in food, plus citrus
fruits or tomatoes for
Vitamin C. Also, if you
are carrying around the
old notion that "false
teeth are less trouble

Symptom or Problem	Cause or What It Means	What to do
		than your own teeth in old age," revise your thinking. Your own teeth are far easier to manage, so save every tooth you've got.

125. *Thyroid Trouble*

Symptom or Problem	Cause or What It Means	What to do
Enlargement of the thyroid and sides of neck (goiter); or over-activity or under-activity for some other reason of this gland, which regulates rates of metabolism and body growth.	Simple goiter (caused by iodine deficiency) announces itself with swelling of the neck. An over-active gland produces too much thyrosin which causes sufferer to become over-active, irritable, tense, excitable. The heart overworks, patient can't rest, spends sleepless nights. The underactive thyroid, on the other hand, makes for slow thinking, thick skin, overweight.	Iodized salt helps to prevent simple goiter in regions where iodine is lacking. For the over-active thyroid, medication or an operation may be necessary to cut secretion of thyroid hormone back to normal. After a thyroidectomy, patient needs calm environment because emotions may still be stirred up. For the underactive thyroid, thyroid extract replacement gets good results.

126. *Peptic Ulcer*

Symptom or Problem	Cause or What It Means	What to do
Erosion of the mucous membrane of the duodenum or stomach caused in part by the corrosive action of the gastric juice.	A raw, sore ulcerous spot in the stomach or intestinal lining, is aggravated by secretion in an excessive amount of hydrochloric acid. At the ulcer's onset, cause may be emotional pressure; later, the ulcer itself may cause a severed blood vessel which makes for hemorrhage. Pain, vomiting and a feeling of	To protect stomach from acid, gastric juice, neutralizing cream and milk are usually given on the hour and bland foods are recommened. (Roughage, highly seasoned foods, aspirin and other stomach irritants are taken away.) Occasionally, an operation is performed, but few effect a real cure unless the patient elimi-

Symptom or Problem   **Cause or What It Means**   **What to do**

emptiness are character-istics. If ulcer perfor-ates, contents of stom-ach may drain into peri-toneal cavity, causing severe pain and shock.

nates the hurry and worry from his life which caused his prob-lem in the first place. Often, a psychiatrist can bring about a change. The most effec-tive drug for reducing hydrochloric acid secre-tion in the stomach and relaxing muscles in the gastrointestinal tract is Belladonna Tincture, U.S.P., or its deriva-tives.

127. *Displaced Uterus*

The womb, in which the prenatal baby rests and de-velops, changes position naturally several times during pregnancy. At other times, unnatural displace-ment can make for a bulging bladder, a dropped cervix, painful menstrua-tion and other in-ternal problems.

Relaxed tissues and muscular injuries during child-bearing are com-mon causes. Occasion-ally, strain or lifting or an inherited weakness may be cause. Discom-fort and feeling of full-ness (which are relieved when woman lies down) will be first signs.

Lacerations should be repaired following childbirth to prevent displacement. Should the uterus be displaced, anyway, backache and internal problems will probably send woman to a doctor, who will insert pessary for sup-port or may recom-mend an operation. Should such a correc-tion be recommended to you, consult an ex-pert gynecologist be-fore having an opera-tion, which can some-times be helpful but may be unnecessary.

128. *Vaccinations be-fore Traveling*

Inoculation with cow pox and shots

Because immunization programs in the United

When you apply for passport, you will be

Symptom or Problem	**Cause or What It Means**	**What to do**
of the modified virus of any of various other diseases are given to travelers heading for a country in which a disease, rare or unknown here, may be prevalent.	States have freed this country of many killer diseasees (and the government wants it that way), you will have a difficult time coming back through customs if you neglect to have recommened shots for wherever you're going. Also, you will avoid catching diseases away from home.	told what diseases to guard against in whatever country you're going to. To save money and time on needed shots, call your local Area Coordinator for the Department of Health and Welfare (listed under United States Government) and ask where shots are given free or for a small fee at a local clinic.

129. *Varicose Veins*

Enlarged, swollen and disfigured veins (usually in the surface area of tho lower limbs) are due to breakdown of valves in veins through which blood flows back to the heart.	May be due to inherited tendency, long years of standing in one position (as a clerk), tumor, pregnancy, overweight, inflammation in deep venous (veins) system.	Obvious relief-givers are: (1) take off weight; (2) change from stand-up to sit-down job; (3) elevate legs on slant board several times a day; (4) improve circulation with contrast baths and/or swimming; (5) massage; (6) wear support hose. For advanced cases: (1) have operation in which problem veins are cut out, forcing blood to recourse; or (2) have injections which will harden in veins, forcing blood to recourse. This is usually of value in controlling small veins after surgery.

130. *Vitamin Deficiency*

Poor night vision, bleeding gums,	A lack of Vitamin A, C, B, D or another vitamin	A balanced diet containing all vitamins nec-

Symptom or Problem   **Cause or What It Means**   **What to do**

nervousness, numbness, weak fingernails or some other physical peculiarity.

or a peculiar inherited dependency on one particular vitamin. (Also, certain physical conditions like alcoholism can make for a vitamin deficiency.)

essary to well being; synthetic vitamins to make up for a deficiency or in case of abnormal physical dependency on a particular vitamin, massive doses of the specific vitamin as needed. Your doctor can help you determine what is needed. Talk to him during a routine checkup before paying out money for vitamins when not necessary.

131. *Worry*

Discomfort from anxious feeling about coming problems or past mistakes can bring on *real* disease.

Uneasy feeling is based either on reality or unreality. For the first, you may be faced with something which is really too big for you, in which case you will have to get help from a banker, lawyer, minister, doctor or other expert.
For the second, you are dreaming up a worry out of habit or because of neurotic fears. Either can cause illness.

If worry is real, ask yourself "What's the worst thing that can happen?" Then, decide what you will do in that case? Chances are the worst *won't* happen but you will be ready. If worry is unreal, and you can see this, talk to a psychiatrist at a local clinic about your tendency to torment yourself. Paying for a session is far less expensive than an ulcer.

132. *Wrinkles*

Creases in the skin are due to diminishing supply of natural oils (sebum) and habitual facial expressions.

Wrinkles are speeded up by the drying effect of the sun, soap and water and by frown and laugh lines. (If you can consciously control frowning, *smile* instead so

Nothing but plastic surgery can stretch out wrinkles, but cleansing with lubricating cream rather than soap and water, plus head down on a slant board a

Symptom or Problem	Cause or What It Means	What to do
	that creases will reflect good cheer.)	couple of times a day to improve circulation can postpone dry skin erosion. Do not overspend for expensive crcreams and lotions. Investigate, and you will find that all ingredients are pretty much the same. Only the perfumes, colors, prices, names and television oommoroialo aro diffor ent.

133. *Wry Neck*

Sometimes called torticollis, wry neck twists neck and head to one side.	Comes from spasms of neck muscles, making for contraction. Rheumatism or a birth defect may be cause.	Massage along contracted muscle in the direction of the heart, take daily stretching exercise to lengthen puckered muscle. If condition is severe, contracted muscle can be lengthened through surgery.

MENTAL ATTITUDE
CAN BRING RELIEF

Your brain is a computer ready to serve you as you will. Feed into it facts relevant to whatever is bothering you plus possible cures and a picture of the result you want, and your brain will help you to find your answer for better health.

If you have a specific problem accept only the true medical facts relevant to whatever is giving you trouble, and throw out all myths and old wives' tales. Then, think through possible cures or relief-givers that you know from reading or observation have helped others. Decide realistically what is most apt to help you. Refuse to dwell on the painful aspects of your condition and decide now you are going to find a way to improve both your physical and mental approach. Within a few days, you will see your course. This is the first step to a cure (or to a better frame of mind, if a cure is not known). This book can help.

HOW TO BRING BACK SOMEONE
WHO IS ALMOST GONE

Basic trouble	Signs	What to do
Loss of blood from external or internal bleeding. (Average body contains six quarts of blood. To lose a quart is harmful; more can mean death.)	Shock and/or low blood pressure	Keep pressure on artery leading to bleeding wound; elevate leg if wound is there. Cover gunshot wound with cloth or plug wound in chest which lets air enter. If nose and mouth are bleeding, raise head and control vomiting.
Insufficient intake of oxygen. (Can result from electric shock, drowning, inhalation of poisonous gas, caved-in chest, choking on foreign object.) Victim takes in too little oxygen to support life, suffers from excess supply of carbon dioxide in tissues.	Pale moist skin, gasping breathing	See that windpipe is clear. Give mouth to mouth resuscitation in open air.

Basic trouble	*Signs*	*What to do*
Internal poisoning	Unconsciousness	Get patient on feet, encourage drinking of milk and water. If patient begins to come to, induce vomiting unless poison is lye or kerosene which must not be drawn into lungs.
External poisoning	Loss of consciousness after snake or insect bite.	Put tourniquet between bite and heart. Get patient to hospital for anti-venom shot.
Third degree burns	Charred skin after plane or train wreck.	Remove clothing not burned into flesh. Cover burns with clean cloth. Keep victim's feet raised.
Traumatic shock due to loss of blood, severe pain, internal fractures or psychological blackout.	Rapid pulse, gasping breathing, weakness.	Elevate feet and legs. Then, raise head. Give fluids if patient becomes conscious. Keep talking to patient, encouraging him to work with you to garner his conscious life force to stay alive.

Even if the heart has stopped, you have five or six minutes in which to restore the beat before the central nervous system and brain are permanently damaged. So don't give up when heart stops. Begin massage immediately. Figure 8-11 following shows the basic technique.

Figure 8-11: Heart Massage. Put one hand on top of the other at middle of breastbone, and apply pressure with heel of bottom hand.

HOW TO GIVE
HEART MASSAGE

To restore heartbeat, place both hands, one on top of the other, on victim's chest at middle of breastbone. Apply pressure with the heel of the bottom hand and push down, not more than two inches into the body, even if this is a large-boned adult. Repeat pressure 60 times in a minute. Effectiveness can be monitored by second person who feels for a peripheral pulse while you push.

[1]Want to know if you (or anyone you are close to) have a real drinking problem? Take (or encourage another) to take this dependency test. For the next six months, see if you can stick to an agreed upon number of drinks a day (one drink, two drinks or three drinks, but no more than three) no matter what happens. If you can do this, you are not an alcoholic, says New York City authority, Marty Mann. If not, you are dependent on alcohol and need help.

[2]Call Alcoholics Anonymous listed in your local directory. Someone who has been in the same boat will help.

[3]To prevent nutritional anemia in teen agers and women, give foods that are rich in iron and help to form red blood corpuscles (live, molasses, green and leafy vegetables, apricots, egg yolks, potatoes, enriched bread and cereals).

[4]See page 228 for complete explanation of your bones, muscles and connective tissue.

[5]See page 221 for complete explanation of your respiratory system.

[6]See page 200 for complete explanation of the urinary system.

[7]See page 228 for complete explanation of your bones, muscles and connective tissue.

[8]See page 222 for complete explanation of blood vessels and heart.

[9]If stool is black but turns red in water, it contains blood. Talk to a doctor.

[10]Occasionally, a glycerine suppository can ease passage of stool.

[11]See page 222 for complete explanation of blood vessels and heart.

[12]See page 226 for complete explanation of hearing apparatus.

[13]See page 229 for complete explanation of endocrine glands.

[14]See page 221 for complete explanation of respiratory system.

[15]See page 219 for complete explanation of digestive system.

[16]See page 225 for complete explanation of brain and nerves.

[17]See page 222 for complete explanation of the heart.

[18]See page 219 for complete explanation of the digestive system.

[19]See page 200 for complete explanation of the urinary system.

[20]See page 226 for complete explanation of the inner ear.

[21]See page 225 for complete explanation of brain and nerve.

[22]See page 225 for complete explanation of brain and nerves.

[23]See page 229 for complete explanation of the endocrine glands.

[24]See page 221 for complete explanation of the respiratory system.

[25]In places like Sun City, Arizona, and Laguna Hills, California, where many retired persons go to live all year in the sunshine, special breathing classes are offered to those who have had lung disorders by doctors at nearby hospitals. In the north, corrective breathing courses are given in many cities by Yoga experts and speech therapists.

[26]See page 231 for complete explanation of the reproductive system.

[27]See page 217 for complete explanation of the skin.

[28]See page 223 for complete explanation of the lymphatic system.

PART THREE

How To Save Up To 90 Percent When You Have Medical Care

**FREE! ONE OF THE MOST WORTHWHILE BOOKS
    YOU WILL EVER SEND FOR**

DISEASES AND PHYSICAL CONDITIONS
Price List: 51A
Superintendent of Documents, Washington, D. C., 20402

The book lists the prices of government publications dealing with sicknesses of all types, contagious and infectious diseases and vital health statistics.

Here are samples: *Identifying Problem Drinkers,* 35¢; *Arthritis and Rheumatism,* 5¢; *Fashion Tips for the Woman with Arthritis,* 20¢; *Birth Defects,* 20¢; *Respiratory Rehabilitation,* 40¢; *What to do About Cancer,* 5¢; *Progress against Leukemia,* 15¢; *Drugs and Narcotics,* 5¢; *Hung on LSD,* 10¢; *Cataract and Glaucoma,* 25¢; *Hardening of the Arteries,* 10¢; *Kidney Diseases,* 15¢; *Mental Retardation,* 15¢; *Smoking and Health,* 5¢; *Veneral Diseases,* 5¢; *Birth and Death Records,* 15¢.

Send card for free directory file; then, send for low-cost publications when you have questions about a problem.

SECOND GOOD SOURCE

Metropolitan Life Insurance Co.
1 Madison Avenue
New York, N. Y., 10010

Free books on various aspects of baby and child care, childhood diseases, alcoholism, cancer, heart disease and the care of older people are available. Ask for books on subject in which you are interested.

9

Foolproof Ways to Avoid Money-Wasting Traps When You Have a Chronic Problem

If someone in your family has rheumatoid arthritis, acne, Parkinson's disease, multiple sclerosis, emphysema or any other chronic or long-term problem, you will be tempted to (1) doctor hop; (2) try every "cure" that you read or hear about; (3) go to quacks. Give in, and the medical merry-go-round will get you nowhere. You will waste money on needless doctor bills, transportation, telephone calls and drugs, but what is even more crucial, you will waste time that you could be spending on therapy. Thus, your disease will become more advanced as you choose cures that never come.

In this chapter, you will find how-to-avoid-a-trap recipes plus specific what-to-do-instead suggestions. Absorb both and you will save time, wear and money.

HOW TO PROCEED WHEN
YOU SUSPECT A CHRONIC DISEASE

When the problem you face may be serious, don't panic. Take this common sense approach.

1. Make an appointment for a complete examination at a hospital or clinic where you can get a special rate. (Students can usually get a special rate at a university clinic; veterans can get help at a veterans hospital; long-time sufferers of polio, leukemia, schizophrenia, etc., can get help from special foundations; church members can get a rate at their church-owned sanitariums; retired actors can get medical help through their organization, so can other professional people.) Think where medical help may be available to you at a special rate through a vocational, social, church or military club. Investigate there.[1]

2. If you can't get an immediate appointment for a thorough examination when you suspect a dangerous disease, like cancer, go at once to a responsible doctor in your town or to the hospital and ask for a biopsy or other verifying test. Let the doctor get you into a special hospital which he can do.

3. Once you know what disease you have, write to all associations and/or foundations that have funds for research in this field.[2] Ask for available free material and for a list of books (with prices) which you can order later. If one or more of these organizations periodically sends out the results of its findings and other material, ask to be put on the mailing list.

4. Read everything that you see about the problem you face but don't grasp for cure-alls advertised by quacks or rush to a new doctor because you feel your present doctor isn't giving you enough attention. Know why you are doing what you are doing, and don't swerve without a reason.

5. Don't send for advertised charms, bracelets, braces, etc., that will do no good. You are too enlightened for voodoo cures. Do respect new findings, but when you think of trying something new, try to look through advertised promises to the product itself. Is there *really* a new ingredient here? Does the reason for the cure make sense?

6. If your disease is a "functional" one that may be psychosomatic in origin, and you know this, confer at least once with a psychologist or psychiatrist at a nearby clinic.[3] (You may get as much from group therapy as from private sessions, which will usually be less expensive.) Work from the first day with the analyst to understand why you may be getting an "escape" or benefit through a particular disease. With this understanding, the need for escape may go.

7. If your doctor recommends physical therapy (hot and cold contrast baths, massage, under-water movements, etc.), pay for some sessions at the hospital, but work again to see how you can duplicate this therapy on your own. With the help of someone at home, you can give yourself hot and cold baths, have massage or get the same effect as massage through exercise and by swimming at a swimming class or a pool open in your town to those in need of therapy.

A chronic or long-term disease can eat dollars by the hundreds by the week and day, yet there is a way to beat this. The key: acceptance of the problem as of now; determination that conditions can be lived with or improved; self reliance. It takes some doing to live with a long-term disease without getting depressed or doing long-term spending, but this can be done.

---

[1]Look in your telephone book under Health Agencies or Associations for a foundation that concentrates on the disease you suspect. Ask for the name of a doctor or clinic in your vicinity that specializes in the disease you are worried about. Also, call your local Visiting Nurse Association which will give you names of local doctors and their specialities, although no specific recommendation can be given. *You will save time, money and worry if you get to the right place first.*

[2]See Chapter 12 for complete list.

[3]Call your County hospital or you United or Community Fund office or your Community Referral system to find out where.

10

Five Sure-Fire Money-Saving Rules the Average Person Never Considers

The average family gives too little attention to preventive medicine and overspends when illness strikes. The reasons: nobody wants to spend more than necessary on doctor bills, and nobody wants to be sick for a day longer than he has to be. Overspending before and after illness strikes helps nothing. With a few money-saving rules, preventive medicine can cost you little and a crisis can be dealt with without monumental expenses. Here are five ways:

1. Take full advantage of free and/or low cost physical examinations.

- When you buy life insurance (and/or in some cases a hospitalization policy), you are requested to take a physical examination for which you do not pay. As an applicant, chances are you do not approach the assigned doctor with the same attitude that you have when you must pay. Not to do so doesn't make sense. The examining doctor isn't doing what he's doing for nothing; he's paid by the insurance company. Next time, ask the insurance company's doctor what you would ask your own doctor in like circumstances. And, if you policy is charged for at a higher than normal rate, ask to see the medical findings. The insurance people have no reason to be secretive; the longer you live, the more they have to gain.

- A free examination may be given to your child in school before going to camp.[1] Examinations will be given to others in your family who may be applying for a new job, entering military service, matriculating at college or going into a special physical fitness program calling for heavy exertion. Should a problem be found, you can ask in most cases to talk to the doctor even if you did not pay. Once again, *somebody* paid . . . prospective employer or the United States government or the college or the club. Knowing what is the matter can help you know what to do. If no problem is reported, you can be pretty sure that the examination revealed nothing abnormal, so you relax until next year when another checkup is wise.

- Sometimes, a free examination can come as the result of your doing work for a hospital or when you sign up to give or sell blood.[2] Or you may be asked to have an examination when you report for strenuous exercise at a local club.[3] If no free examination comes to you in the natural couse of your everyday life, pay to get *the most thorough examination*[4] *you can get in your town or county.* Call the local office of the American Cancer Association and ask if there is either a permanent or temporary cancer detection clinic nearby. The cost for a complete examination there may be higher than what you will pay at a general practitioner's office in order to cover lab fees and special tests, but the examination will be deep and thorough. Should the tests uncover a problem, you will save money in the long run and have a far better chance of staying physically fit for years.

2. Encourage everyone in your family to take advantage of low cost physical fitness programs near your home. Here are programs to look for:

- Private schools in some communities open their gyms or pools to local residents for certain programs. In New

Milford, Connecticut, Canterbury Prep School opens its swimming pool during the winter months to local people in need of "therapy." The cost is nominal, $15 for 10 hour-long sessions in a huge, handsome, well-heated pool. The Community Center offers the program through the town's recreation department and does not define therapy as something needed only by the severely handicapped.

- Through either the YMCA and/or YWCA or YMHA in many cities, whether either has a swimming pool, swimming is available on the premises or through another organization's facilities. For low cost, open gym classes, weight lifting, coed badminton and judo are available. In a "Y" without gym and swimming facilities, the cost for 12 lessons in a given program may be as low as $8. Where there are full facilities, young members pay $12 a year for participation in all programs. Adult members pay in the neighborhood of $32 a year for full participation.

- In many places, family hiking clubs are arranged through local recreation department's churches and clubs. In New York City, indoor and outdoor swimming pools are open year round. Church groups sponsor camps for all ages; Head Start plans summer activity programs as well as pre-school work for very young children.[5]

- Make a list of as many activities in your town that you can find that are available to your age group and that of each of your children. As a start, call your local "Ys", Boy Scouts, Girl Scouts, Camp Fire Girls, Jewish Community Center, your church, a school counselor, your town's recreation director and/or superintendent of parks. You will find more activities than you knew anything about, and hopefully you will find many that the various members of your family will enjoy. Do not force the issue but keep looking until you find at least one physical fitness activity that is interesting to each person.

3. Make every doctor's appointment do the work of three. Unless you plan ahead, you will overspend on routine medical care. One day, you will take your baby to a pediatrician for a measles shot; a few days later, you will send your teen-age son to another doctor for a booster

company only if not paid by another. The reason: a man who is heavily insured by several companies may be able to earn more through disability coverage than through working; therefore, he has no motivation to go back to work. To avoid overlap, check your policies with the help of an insurance advisor.[8]

- Group policies through membership in a particular professional club or through your business, AAA or a travel group are far less expensive than a policy you buy on your own and sometimes offer accident and sickness policies which pay benefits even when there is duplication. Check before you buy more.

- A sound program for most families, whether buying on their own or through a group, is an investment in a Blue Cross and Blue Shield contract which pays for hospitalization and medical care for a restricted time, a major medical plan with a $500 deductible clause which takes over where Blue Cross leaves off, special sickness and health policies which give income coverage should a man's or woman's earning power be cut short.

- General rule: Buy through a group and often you can save up to 60 percent on your premiums.[9]

- Something to remember: Your Blue Shield contract is terminated on the day you become eligible for Medicare, which offers similar benefits. Most major medical policies, written now, are not written for life but only until the subscriber is eligible for Medicare.

- Two warnings: Carry your Blue Shield indentification card and number, and major medical insurance policy identification card and number with you at all times; also, never be without your American Automobile Association card on which is printed that policy number.[10] *And keep your actual policies at home, not in your safety deposit box.* In case of emergency, an outsider may not be able to get into your safety deposit box to produce your policies; in the meantime, you will need help.

- Keep an accurate list of your insurance policies, including payment dates in a special Cash Book at home. When you receive benefits, enter here. Then, when you figure your annual income tax be sure to take as a deduction what you are entitled to, as follows:

.. Deduct one half of what you pay out for premiums for medical insurance, not to exceed $150.

.. Add the remaining amount to your total figure for medical protection and expenses.

.. Add up everything you pay for drugs or medicines during the year, and deduct all you spend over one percent of your total taxable income.

.. Add up all doctor and dental charges, visiting nurse and other nursing fees not reimbursed by your insurance coverage, therapeutic massages and the remaining health and medical insurance not already deducted. Figure what you spend for transportation to doctors, dentists, etc., at six cents a mile.[11] Whatever you spend in any given year that exceeds three precent of your annual taxable income is deductible. If you have a bad year from a health standpoint, deducations on your income tax can help to compensate.

5. Insist on the best possible care for older members of your family, but don't overspend.

● Let's say that you have an older parent living with you and, also, two children. If you pay food and household expenses for all, you can count your parent as an income tax deduction if what you pay out is more than what she collects in social security.[12]

● Whether either of your parents lives with you at the time of retirement find out with them what social security benefits they are entitled to. On the address side of a government post card, type Social Security Administration, Baltimore 35, Maryland. On the other side, put your parent's social security number with a request that you be sent a record of wages and self-employed income credited to this account. Take this to the nearest Social Security office. What is due to come in will be explained. While at the office, get a booklet informing you about Medicare and Medicaid. Help your parents make plans for the future with these benefits in mind.

[1]In most states, periodic checkups are given in public schools at least every three years—in kindergarten and in third, sixth, ninth and twelfth grades. Here, the school pays a local doctor to do the examining unless the parent does not or cannot get the child to a private doctor by the designated date. Findings are given to parents if a problem is uncovered. When going to a private camp, your child usually is asked to have an American Camping Association form filled out by a doctor. Should he win or be given a vacation at a church or community camp, he will be given the examination free.

[2]In the Red Cross Bloodmobile or at a commercial blood bank where, in the first instance, you give blood and, in the second, sell it for an average of $6 a pint for Rh positive blood and $10 a pint for Rh negative blood, you will be weighed and given a hemoglobin and a simple heart examination. Here, you will not be accepted as a donor unless pronounced O.K.

[3]For a strenuous exercise class at the "Y" or other club, you usually will be asked to bring an O.K. from your doctor; however, today, when there is a shortage of doctors, you may be examined along with several others at the club, and the charge will be paid for by the organization and added to your fee.

[4]In New York City, the Preventive Medicine Institute, Strang Clinic, located at 55 East 34th Street, gives a thorough examination for cancer, heart, stroke susceptibility, glaucoma and anything else that may be the matter. First-time fee, $70; after that, the fee is $60. Write or call for an appointment two to three weeks in advance. All cities do not have such a clinic, but in many there is a temporary or permanent cancer detection program partially underwritten by the American Cancer Society which is set up in a local hospital or other headquarters. In some, as at Strang, you can get a complete examination as you take tests for cancer. This is ideal.

[5]Parents of Head Start children may or may not be on welfare. However, there is an income level for parents which is low. (Exception: a ten percent enrollment of children whose family income may exceed the maximum but who have health or environmental need is allowed.)

[6]You think the chest pain means a heart attack, but after tests at the hospital, the chest pain turns out to be a referral pain from a chronic arthritic condition of the spine.

[7]Only 38 percent of our present physicians can be classified as family doctors, so be grateful if there are enough to go around in your town. Recently, the state of Washington has inaugurated MEDEX which puts to work as doctors' assistants highly qualified medics and corpsmen discharged from the armed forces. Former battlefield workers stitch up cuts, apply casts and make preliminary assessments of patients' ailments. Such a program could be our national answer to the doctor shortage, and the pilot project is being analyzed with this in mind.

[8]When you buy a policy on your own, ask before signing that all your health and accident and disability policies be looked at by a reputable advisor from a reputable company. He will do this because he stands to gain if he finds a hole in your coverage.

[9]While company plans differ, you can count on a substantial savings over what you would pay for the same coverage as an individual. Investigate club and group plans before buying on your own.

[10]Should you have an accident calling for AAA assistance on the highway, no service will be given unless you have your card. (Your number is not enough.) Also, your AAA accident policy should be at home with your other policies.

[11]Put down cost for ambulance, plane, train or bus to get medical care and cost of gasoline, toll fares, etc., to go by car—or figure a straight six cents a mile, which will be allowed.

[12]In this case, divide your food and household expenses by five. This will tell you what you are spending for the support of each person. Also, figure what you are spending for drugs and medicines for your parent not covered by Medicare. Does the total you spend for her food and living expenses, plus health care exceed what she takes in for social security? You are entitled to deduct this excess from your taxable income.

11

Where to Go for Special Services Your Taxes Help to Support

Right today, you may hear a TV or radio announcement (or read a newspaper story) urging you to take a preventive step to help your child avoid a specific disease or epidemic. If you have questions, call your town's Visiting Nurse Association or nearest child care center listed under your town's Department of Health. Give your name and address and ask if the vaccine you have been advised to get is free to all. If yes, ask where to take your child. Chances are the answer will be, "He can have it in school," or "Go to the child care clinic nearest to you."

Now, if you would like to have the free service and vaccine but want your doctor's approval, call and ask his receptionist or nurse (or the doctor himself) if he is recommending the vaccine which is being campaigned for. If the answer is yes, you have the assurance you want. Give your child a note of approval if the vaccine is being given at school. And don't worry about your child's being afraid if you are not there. He will be less anxious lined up for vaccine along with all the "kids" than he would be if he were alone in a doctor's office with you.

WHAT IF YOU CAN AFFORD TO PAY?

The only person who stands to gain if you pay for an examination or vaccine offered free to all is your doctor, and chances are he's so busy he would prefer to have you go to the school or clinic for this service, anyway. The doctor who gives your child the vaccine at a school or clinic receives pay for his services, and you pay in taxes.

A percentage of every tax dollar you pay goes to the Department of Health, Education and Welfare in Washington, D. C., for just such purposes as the rubella effort. Then, money is given to states and cities in the form of grants for specific campaigns and services. As far as the government is concerned, you are entitled to a service as offered, but always remember this: the purpose of a campaign is *not charity but prevention.* If an epidemic cannot be averted, a crisis will come and everyone will pay.[1] That is the reason for the *free* vaccine or examination in any preventive effort. The government isn't giving you anything, it wants your help!

MANY DIAGNOSTIC SERVICES
ARE FREE

Sometime this year, you will probably see a sign in a window in your town urging you to have an eye examination for glaucoma. Or you may read a newspaper story sometime in November about how to send for a free urinalysis by mail in a "stop diabetes" campaign. Or someone will come to your front door and offer to give your child a free blood test for lead poisoning. Or a van will be parked in your town which contains X-rays and equipment for taking Pap tests of the cervix in a cancer detection effort.

The first may be sponsored by the National Association for the Prevention of Blindness; the second, by your state's Department of Public Health in cooperation with the American Diabetes Association; the third, by your city's Public Health Department; the fourth, by this same department in cooperation with the American Cancer Society. Except in rare cases, you are eligible for each examination at no cost or for a minimum fee, whatever your income. The same holds true for X-rays in stop emphysema and air pollution drives, for examination in syphilis detection and tuberculosis prevention efforts.

The examination in any giant campaign is simple, accurate and efficient. For glaucoma examinations, temporary eye examining facilities are usually set up in a local building; the whole procedure takes only a few minutes. For diabetes detection, today, you do not even see a doctor and you can mail in a urine specimen without a bottle.[2] For the detection of lead poisoning in a child, which comes from chewing on toys and other plastered and painted objects containing lead, a sample of blood is taken in seconds in the home and is invaluable because it can uncover anemia-as well as lead poisoning. As for the Pap test, that takes only a minute or two and can detect cancer in its beginning stages when it can be controlled.

Early detection of lead poisoning can prevent encephalitis (inflammation of the brain'), and early detection of diabetes, cancer, syphilis and tuberculosis can prevent disability and/or early death. When you are urged to have a free examination, *go!*

WHY THE GOVERNMENT WANTS YOU TO HAVE THESE FREE EXAMINATIONS

Many advocates of preventive medicine urge regular compulsory examinations for every citizen of the United States to detect diseases that can be debilitating and/or fatal later on. Such examinations, of course, would be free. Their reasoning: any disease that lays low one member of the family makes for giant hospital and doctor bills which eventually have to be paid by an individual or through Medicare, insurance or welfare. Wherever the money comes from, it takes away from positive spending in another direction. Thus, while mass examinations may be costly at first glance, they mean far less expense for the government (and the individual who supports that government) at a later date.

Today, most "free examinations" in the United States call for voluntary participation. As you consider, remember this: the government wants you to take part or it would not allocate funds through the Department of Health, Education and Welfare for these special programs. You are helping when you participate, just as you help the government when you fill out your Census form. And the benefits to you are immense.

OTHER FREE SERVICES

Foundations have been set up by individuals, colleges, private companies and associations to help in the rehabilitation of persons affected by a crippling disease and/or chronic disability. Through such a foundation, you can get rehabilitation help (in or out of a hospital) for someone in your family afflicted with multiple sclerosis, infantile paralysis, cerebral palsy or any of a dozen other debilitating diseases Sometimes, these foundations receive additional funds from the government or through fund-raising drives. The service given to an individual may be free or decided upon by a particular foundation according to a given family's ability to pay.

If your child is crippled or has a chronic disease that can be helped if treatment is made available, ask the doctor who made the original diagnosis about special hospitals, sanitariums and treatment centers located near you or in another part of the country. Then, do some sleuthing on your own. Write for literature to the Multiple Sclerosis Society, the National Foundation for Infantile Paralysis (or Georgia Warm Springs Foundation), the Arthritis Foundation, the United Cerebral Palsy Associations or to any other organization devoted to the study and care of the disease you want to know about.[3] Information from this first source will lead you to centers and clinics where you can get more information. Eventually, you will know what help you can get for what price. Should you find that your child can be benefited from long-term treatment in a hospital or sanitarium far from home, do not hold back because you do not want to leave home. The hospitals are set up to help children just like yours. *Give him his chance.*

DEPEND ON YOUR LOCAL VISITING NURSE ASSOCIATION

Take advantage of services offered by your *Visiting Nurse Association.* Look under the V's in your telephone book and call when you want (1) information about where to go in your town to get brochures and other information about a particular disease; and (2) help in a family situation where one or more members may be temporarily incapacitated or chronically ill.

Case history: A family we know consists of a mother, two teen-agers and a father who has multiple sclerosis. This father is able to do bookkeeping jobs at home but he is unable to move around without help. The mother has to work away from home to support her family, so who can help her husband go to the bathroom and to the kitchen for lunch at noon? With the help of a Visiting Nurse, he can take care of himself until the children come home from school. The cost is figured on the family's ability to pay.[4]

Should you be faced with an emergency or long-time illness in your home, call your Visiting Nurse Association. Someone will come to talk with you and, later, to your doctor who is acquainted with the needs of your family. If you are eligible for service (and physical need is the criterion), this is a real money saver, even if you pay the top fee. In most cities, the Visiting Nurse program is supported by fees, an appropriation from the town, which you help to support with taxes, and by the United Fund, which you have helped to support with contributions. Again, this service is supported by you and is available to you. Take advantage.

THERE IS MORE HELP
THAN YOU KNOW

When a welfare mother needs the help of various agencies, she gets the services she needs through the intervention of a social worker. The average mother does not have this guidance, but she can make her own search and should *when trouble strikes.* Otherwise, she will pay the full price for whatever is needed each step of the way, and the cost of a simple illness may be astronomical. To get what she needs all she has to do is to take advantage of help that she is entitled to, but sometimes that is difficult to find. Certainly, however, the results of the search are worth the doing. Should you need help in an emergency, use the available services that you have helped to pay for. By so doing, you can save thousands of dollars you might otherwise have to spend.

---

[1]In 1969, an epidemic of rubella (German Measles) was responsible for the deaths of 30,000 unborn children and the births of 20,000 deformed children. The next year, a brilliant campaign by New York City's Health Department resulted in the inoculation of 530,000 children and warded off another epidemic.

[2]Each fall, the state health department in most states distribute thousands of "diabetes dri-pak kits" which they buy from the American Diabetes Association, 18 E. 48th Street, New York, N. Y., 10017, and distribute free to doctors, pharmacists and visiting nurses in towns and cities in the state. Individuals are urged to pick up a kit,

containing blotting paper which is to be wet at home with urine and mailed to the state capital for a free sugar test. Should you do this, you will be notified if your urine contains sugar and you can then go to your doctor for confirmation.

[3]See Chapter 12 for a list of associations which send free material on request.

[4]In our town, the service of a Visiting Nurse may be free or charged for at the rate of $9.17 a call or lower. There is no time limit per call; the nurse stays as needed.

Free: *Invaluable book from American Medical Association*

Figure 12-1: An important book for you.

Tells where to get information pertaining
to 33 different diseases and/or disabilities.

Write to: National Health Council
              1740 Broadway
              New York, N. Y., 10019
              or
              National Social Welfare Assembly
              345 East 46th Street
              New York, N. Y., 10017

12

101 Places to Get Free Medical Information That Can Save You Thousands of Dollars

"An investment in knowledge," said Benjamin Franklin, "pays the best interest." This is never more true than when you are searching for the best medical help you can get for someone in your family who is suffering from a condition you know little about. Know more, and you will not spend money for useless high-priced medicines, quack promises or for expensive conferences with a self-appointed "specialist" who is not as qualified as he should be to deal with the disease with which you are afflicted. By knowing the nature of a specific disease, you can avoid being taken in by phonies.

Here are 101 national associations dedicated to researching and getting information (and help) into the hands of afflicted persons and their families. Many of these organizations spend millions every year for research, so you will benefit from new findings.

Also, many provide secondary services like free examinations, camps for handicapped children, books in braille for the blind at cost, schooling in lip reading for the deaf, rehabilitation centers for the handicapped, classes for expectant mothers, arrange for transplants and do other countless services. To get information about the disease, itself, and what's new from research, plus a list of clinics or hospitals near you where you can go for therapy, simply write a government card with a message like this.

On side for address: Institute for the Crippled and Disabled
                         400 First Avenue
                         New York, New York 10010

On back side: My child is a seven-year-old deaf mute.
                         Please send me brochures and/or period-
                         icals about the services you offer. Also,
                         send me suggestions which you may have
                         for educational and vocational treatment
                         and advice for rehabilitation.
                         Thank you.

                                              Your name,
                                              Address

101 ASSOCIATIONS

Accident Prevention

Employers Insurance of WAUSAU, 485 Lexington Ave., New York, N. Y.
National Safety Council, 425 N. Michigan Ave., Chicago, Ill., 60611

Aged

National Council of Senior Citizens, 1627 K St., N.W., Washington, D.C.
National Council on the Aging, 315 Park Ave. S., New York, N. Y., 10010
Public Affairs Committee, Inc., 381 Park Ave. S., New York, N. Y., 10016

Alcoholism

Al-Anon Family Group Headquarters, 200 Park Ave. S., New York, N. Y.,
Alcoholics Anonymous, Box 459, Grand Central Annex, New York, N. Y.,
    10017
National Committee for the Prevention of Alcoholism, 6830 Laurel St., N.
    W., Washington 12, D. C.
National Council on Alcoholism, Inc., 2 Park Ave., New York, N. Y., 10017

National Institute of Mental Health, Public Health Service, Department of Health, Education and Welfare, Bethesda, Md., 2020014

Allergic Diseases

Allergy Foundation of America, 801 2nd Ave., New York, N. Y., 10017

Arthritis and Rheumatism

National Institute of Arthritis and Metabolic Diseases, Bldg. 31, Room 9A04, National Institute of Health, Bethesda, Md.
The Arthritis Foundation, 1212 Ave. of the Americas, New York, N. Y., 10036

Asthma

Children's Asthma Research Institute & Hospital at Denver, 3447 W. 19th Street, Denver 4, Colorado
National Foundation for Asthmatic Children at Tucson, 5601 Trails End, Tucson, Arizona

Birth Defects

The National Foundation—March of Dimes, 800 Second Ave., New York, N. Y., 10017

Blindness and Sight

American Association of Ophthalmology, 1100 17th St., N. W., Washington, D. C., 20036
American Association of Instructions of the Blind, 711 14th St., N. W., Washington, D. C., 20005
American Foundation for the Blind, 15 W. 16th St., New York, N. Y., 10011
American Printing House for the Blind, 1839 Frankfort Ave., P. O. Box 6085, Louisville 6, Ky.
Association for Advancement of Blind Children, 520 5th Ave., New York, N. Y., 10036
Braille Institute of America, Inc., 741 N. Vermont Ave., Los Angeles, Calif., 90029
Christian Record Braille Foundation, 4444 S. 52nd St., Lincoln, Neb., 68516
Eye Bank for Sight Restoration, Inc., 210 E. 64th St., New York, N. Y., 10021
Fight for Sight, 41 W. 57th St., New York, N. Y., 10019
Guiding Eyes for the Blind, 106 E. 41st St., New York, N. Y., 10017
Institute for Glaucoma Research, 667 Madison Ave., New York, N. Y.
National Aid to Visually Handicapped, 3201 Balboa St., San Francisco, Calif., 94121
National Center for Chronic Disease Control, 4040 N. Fairfax Dr., Arlington, Va., 22203

National Council to Combat Blindness, Inc., 41 W. 57th St., New York, N. Y., 10019

National Federation of the Blind, 2652 Shasta Rd., Berkeley, Calif., 94708

National Industries for the Blind, 1120 Ave. of the Americas, New York, N. Y., 10019

National Society for the Prevention of Blindness, Inc., 79 Madison Ave., New York, N. Y., 10016

Research to Prevent Blindness, Inc., 598 Madison Ave., New York N. Y., 10022

The Seeing-Eye, Inc., Washington Valley Rd., Morristown, N. J.

Brain

Brain Research Foundation, Inc., 939 E. 57th St., Chicago, Ill., 60637

Cancer

American Cancer Society, Inc., 219 E. 42nd St., New York, N. Y., 10017

Cancer Aid For All, 44 E. 53rd St., New York, N. Y.

Cancer Care, Inc., 1 Park Ave., New York, N. Y.

The Damon Runyon Memorial Fund for Cancer Research, Inc., 33 W. 56th St., New York, 10019

Cerebral Palsy

Cerebral Palsy Recreation Center, 652 W. 170th St., New York, N. Y.

United Cerebral Palsy Associations, Inc., 321 W. 44th St., New York, N. Y., 10036

Child Care

American Institute of Child Care Centers, 25 N. Eola Dr., Orlando, Fla., 32801

National Committee for Children & Youth, 1145 19th St., N. W., Washington, D. C., 20036

Chronic and Crippling Diseases

Disabled American Veterans, 1425 E. McMillan St., Cincinnati, Ohio, 45206

Goodwill Industries of America, 1913 N St., N. W., Washington, D. C., 20006

Institute for the Crippled and Disabled, 400 First Ave., New York, N. Y., 10010

National Amputation Foundation, 12-45 150th St., Whitestone, N. Y., 11357

National Society for Crippled Children and Adults, 2023 W. Ogden Ave., Chicago, Ill., 60612

Shut-in Society, Inc., 11 W. 42nd St., New York, N. Y., 10036

Cleft Palate

American Cleft Palate Association, Parker Hall, University of Missouri, Columbia, Mo., 65202

Cystic Fibrosis

National Cystic Fibrosis Research Foundation, 175 Fifth Ave., New York, N. Y.

Deafness and Hearing

Alexander Graham Bell Association for the Deaf, 1537 36th St., N. W., Washington, D. C., 20007

Deafness Research Foundation, 366 Madison Ave., New York, N. Y., 10017

National Association of Hearing and Speech Agencies, 919 18th St., N. W., Washington, D. C., 20006

National Association of the Deaf, 2025 Eye St., N. W., Washington, D. C., 20006

Diabetes

American Diabetes Association, Inc., 18 E. 48th St., New York, N. Y., 10017

Diabetes Foundation, Inc., 170 Pilgrim Rd., Boston, Mass., 02215

Emphysema

Emphysema Anonymous, 1363 Palmetto Ave., Ft. Myers, Fla., 33901

Task Force on Emphysema and Chronic Bronchitis, c/o National Tuberculosis Association, 1740 Broadway, New York, N. Y., 10019

Epilepsy

Epilepsy Foundation of America, 1419 H St., N. W., Washington, D. C., 20005

Health Organizations

American Medical Association—Education and Research Foundation, 535 N. Dearborn St., Chicago, Ill., 60610

Medic-Alert Foundation International, 1000 N. Palm, Turlock, Calif., 95380

National Health Council, 1740 Broadway, New York, N. Y., 10019

The American National Red Cross, Washington, D. C., 20006

The People-to-People Health Foundation, Inc., Project HOPE, 2233 Wisconsin Ave., N. W., Washington, D. C., 20007

United Health Foundations, Inc., 820 Second Ave., New York, N. Y., 10017

Heart Disease

American Heart Association, Inc., 44 E. 23rd St., New York, N. Y., 10010

Heart Information Center, National Heart Institute, Bethesda, Md., 20014

Hemophilia

National Hemophilia Foundation, 25 W. 39th St., New York, N. Y., 10018

Infantile Paralysis

Georgia Warm Springs Foundation, 120 Broadway, New York, N. Y., 10005

Kidney Disease

National Kidney Foundation, Inc., 315 Park Ave. S., New York, N. Y., 10010

Leprosy

Leonard Wood Memorial for the Eradication of Leprosy, 79 Madison Ave., New York, N. Y., 10016

Leukemia

Leukemia Society of America, Inc., 211 E. 43rd St., New York, N. Y., 10017

Maternal Health

American Association for Maternal & Child Health, Inc., 116 S. Michigan Ave., Suite 703, Chicago, Ill., 60603
Maternity Center Association, 48 E. 92nd St., New York, N. Y., 10028

Medical Research

National Society for Medical Research, 1330 Massachusetts Ave., N. W., Suite 103, Washington, D. C., 20005

Mental Health

American Association of Psychiatric Clinics for Children, 250 W. 57th St., New York, N. Y., 10019
American Mental Health Foundation, 2 E. 86th St., New York, N. Y., 10028
American Psychiatric Association, 1700 18th St., N. W., Washington, D. C., 20009
Association for Mentally Ill Children, 12 W. 12th St., New York, N. Y.
Children's Bureau, Social Security Administration, U. S. Department of Health, Education and Welfare, Washington, D. C., 20025
The National Association for Mental Health, Inc., 10 Columbus Circle, New York, N. Y., 10019

Multiple Sclerosis

National Multiple Sclerosis Society, 257 Park Ave. S., New York, N. Y., 10010

Muscular Dystrophy

Muscular Dystrophy Associations of America, Inc., 1790 Broadway, New York, N. Y., 10019

Myasthenia Gravis

The Myasthenia Gravis Foundation, Inc., 2 E. 103rd St., New York, N. Y., 10029

Narcotics

Addicts Anonymous, Box 2000, Lexington, Ky.
International Federation for Narcotic Education, 918 F St., N. W., Washington, D. C., 20004
Narcotics Education, 6830 Laurel Ave., Washington, D. C., 20012
National Association for the Prevention of Narcotics, 305 E. 79th St., New York, N. Y.

Neuromuscular Diseases

The National Foundation for Neuromuscular Diseases, Inc., 250 W. 57th St., New York, N. Y., 10019

Nutrition

American Dietetic Association, 620 N. Michigan Ave., Chicago, 11, Ill.
Food and Nutrition Board, 2101 Constitution Ave., Washington, D. C., 20025

Paraplegia

National Paraplegia Foundation, 333 N. Michigan Ave., Chicago, Ill., 60601

Parkinson's Disease

Parkinson's Disease Foundation, New York Neurological Institute, 710 W. 168th St., New York, N. Y., 10032

Pituitary

National Pituitary Agency, 8 S. Eutaw St., Baltimore, Md., 21201

Reducing

Buxom Bells, International, 1392 Grayton Rd., Grosse Pointe Park, Mich., 48230
Tops Club, 4575 S. 5th St., Milwaukee, Wis., 53207

Rehabilitation

American Rehabilitation Committee, Inc., 28 E. 21st St., New York, N. Y., 10010
American Rehabilitation Foundation, Inc., Kenny Rehabilitation Institute, 1800 Chicago Ave., Minneapolis, Minn., 55404
Association of Rehabilitation Centers, 828 Davis St., Evanston, Ill., 60201
Audiology and Speech Correction Center, Walter Reed Army Hospital, Washington, D. C., 20012
Comeback, Inc., 945 5th Ave., New York, N. Y.
National Rehabilitation Association, 1029 Vermont Ave., N. W., Washington, D. C., 20005

New York University—Bellevue Medical Center, Institute of Physical Medicine and Rehabilitation, 400 E. 34th St., New York, N. Y., 10016

Retarded Children

Association for the Help of Retarded Children, 200 Park Ave. S., New York, N. Y.

National Association for Retarded Children, 420 Lexington Ave., New York, N. Y., 10017

Retarded Infants Services, Inc., 386 Park Ave. S., New York, N. Y., 10016

Sex Education

Sex Information and Education Council of the U. S., 1855 Broadway, New York, N. Y., 10023

Sterility

Planned Parenthood—World Population, 515 Madison Ave., New York, N. Y., 10022

Tuberculosis

National Tuberculosis and Respiratory Disease Association, 1740 Broadway, New York, N. Y., 10019

Unmarried Mothers

Florence Crittenton Homes Association, Inc., 608 E. Dearborn St., Chicago, Ill., 60605

Margaret Sanger Research Foundation, 17 W. 16th St., New York, N. Y., 10011

National Association on Service to Unmarried Parents, 171 W. 12th St., New York, N. Y., 10011

National Council of Illegitimacy, 44 E. 23rd St., New York, N. Y., 10010

Public Affairs Committee, 381 Park Ave. S., New York, N. Y., 10016

Venereal Diseases

American Social Health Association, 1740 Broadway, New York, N. Y., 10019

A few of these associations are supported by foundations set up by privately owned companies and/or individuals. The others are supported by contributions, fees for services and by government grants which you help to finance. Funds in the latter case are allocated according to the number of persons an association reaches in a year, so your call is welcome. Somewhere, there is a service that will help you to a better understanding of any disease or disability you want to know more about. Finding out where is usually as close as your telephone book.

PART FOUR

How Your Body Functions

13

Simplified Explanations
of 11 Body Systems

The human body is a single organism composed of separate (but related) "systems." On this and the following pages, the skin, heart, brain, muscles and other units are explained separately. When the body is functioning as Nature intended, all systems work as one.

YOUR SKIN:
THE PROTECTIVE ENVELOPE
THAT COVERS YOUR BODY

The body is contained in a sack or envelope of skin weighing about seven pounds in an adult.

Two kinds of tissue make up the skin: the outside layers—the epidermis—and strong inner layers of connective tissue—the dermis. The outermost layer is made of dead cells which protect the whole body. Beneath it, the germinating layer constantly undergoes cell division, new cells moving up to replace those shed off the external layer.

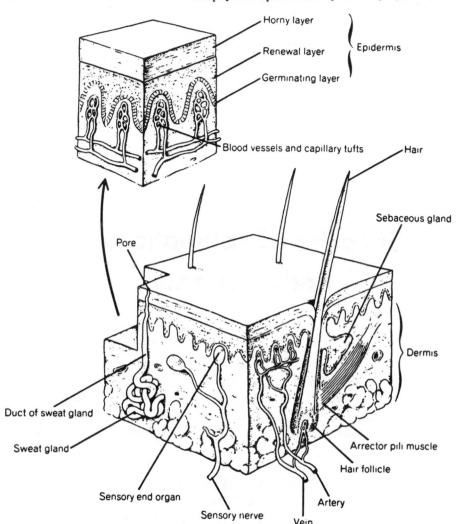

Figure 13-2: Cross-Section of Your Skin Figure

The dermis is filled with a rich bed of blood vessels and capillary tufts which carry the blood near the surface and help to control body temperature. In hot weather blood flows rapidly, carrying away heat; in winter the flow slows down and heat is conserved. Sweat from sweat glands eleminates wastes and cools the surface by evaporation. Sebaceous glands in the dermis secrete oils that keep the hair from drying out and form a protective film on the skin.

FOR FUEL AND GROWTH:
THE DIGESTIVE SYSTEM

Starting at the mouth, the digestive system (which converts food into fuel) forms a continuous tube through which the food is churned and moved. Along the way are stations where chemicals produced by the body are added to help break the raw materials into basic molecular units. One such station is the pancreas, where secretions break down proteins, carbohydrates and fats. Another is the liver, which produces bile to aid in the digestion and absorption of fat. The gall bladder, a pear-shaped sac, stores bile. Some of the fuel units which result may be simple like sugar molecules, or complex like proteins. All are small enough to pass through the lining of the small intestine and, then, to travel with blood and lymph fluid to the cells of the body. Water is absorbed into the blood through the capillaries of the large intestine.

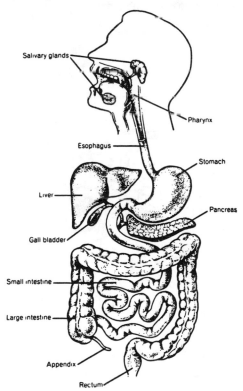

Figure 13-3: Digestive System

FOR PURIFICATION:
THE URINARY SYSTEM

Each kidney contains a million tiny filtering units called nephrons for purifying the circulating blood. Part of the nephron is a tuft of capillaries covered by a membrane shaped like a basket. This is called the glomerulus, and in it water and soluble materials are filtered from the blood. The purified blood passes out through the renal vein.

The glomerulus is connected to a series of tubes that reabsorb water and other materials the body can utilize. The waste products are collected by tubules that take it to the renal pelvis for disposal. This waste liquid descends through the ureters, two long tubes, each leading from a kidney to the bladder. Eventually, the bladder signals the nervous system that it is sufficiently distended to require being emptied through the urethra.

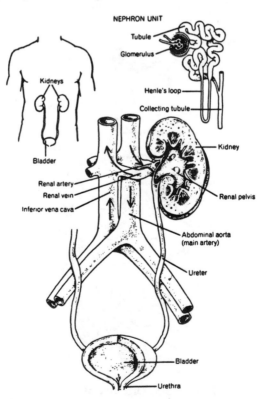

Figure 13-4: The Urinary System

TO HELP PRODUCE ENERGY:
YOUR RESPIRATORY SYSTEM

The nutrients in each cell burn by combining with oxygen provided by the respiratory system. This process, which is slowed up by body chemicals, releases carbon dioxide which is breathed out.

When the diaphragm contracts on inhaling, the rib cage expands and causes a partial vacuum in the lungs. Because the pressure outside the body is now greater than inside, air is pushed into the nose, where it is warmed and humidified as it passes through internal scroll-like passageways. It is dry-cleaned by tiny hairs that catch particles and wet cleaned by mucous lined walls.

The cleansed air passes through the pharynx (tube from nose) and the larynx (voice box) to descend through the trachea (windpipe) which is divided into a bronchus leading to each lung. The branches of the bronchi become smaller and smaller until these passages end in tiny air cells, bunched like grapes, that are called alveoli.

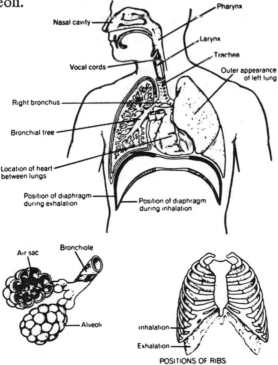

Figure 13-5: The Respiratory System

Oxygen passes through the tissues of the alveoli, rich with capillary arteries, to be transported through the blood stream to the cells, where oxidation takes place. During exhalation, the process is reversed. Carbon dioxide from the capillaries of the alveoli passes into the air sacs, where it is expelled.

PIPELINE FOR YOUR BLOOD:
YOUR BLOOD VESSELS AND HEART

Many blood vessels are finer than a hair. The walls of these tiny vessels (or capillaries) are often a single layer of cells, so that nutrients and other products, picked up through the walls of the intestine, can pass through the blood stream and flow to all parts of the body.

The tiny capilaries bring blood into contact with almost all tissues and from the connection between the arteries and veins which carry blood away from and to the heart.

Capillaries connect with tiny venules and arterioles, which merge with larger and larger veins and arteries. Two large veins, the superior and inferior vena cavae, carrying blood that has exhausted its oxygen supply, enter the right atrium, one of the four compartments of the heart. From the right atrium, the unoxygenated blood flows to the right ventricle, where it is pumped out through the pulmonary arteries to the lungs. There it leaves carbon dioxide (to be breathed out), absorbs oxygen and flows back through the pulmonary veins to the heart, entering the left atrium. From here it flows to the left ventricle and starts another trip through the aorta and the veins, distributing oxygenated blood throughout the body.

About half of the blood volume is made up of solid parts called red blood cells, white blood cells and platelets. Because the red blood cells contain a chemical substance called hemoglobin, they can pick up oxygen and carbon dioxide for transport. By changing shape, the white blood cells move about and can chase and engulf bacteria. Platelets help blood coagulate by forming fibrin, a network of fibers that trap blood cells and form a dam to hold back any further escape of blood from a scratch or wound.

The liquid half of the blood is made up of a watery fluid called plasma. In it are hundreds of different substances in suspension or solution, including blood-clotting proteins, antibodies, hormones, enzymes, minerals and nutrients. Mixed with the plasma is another fluid—lymph—which carries these substances through the capillary walls and constantly bathes the cells of our body.

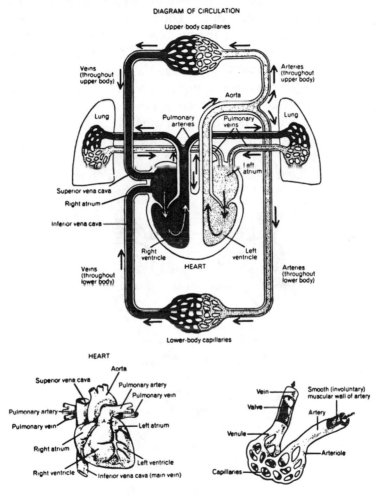

Figure 13-6: The Blood Vessels and Heart

FOR YOUR OVERALL PROTECTION:
THE LYMPHATIC SYSTEM

After bathing all of the cells, the lymph fluid returns to the blood stream. After delivering its nutrients to the cells, it picks up their waste and passes into myriad lymph capillaries. These merge with larger and larger tubes in the manner of blood vessels to form the lymphatic system.

Most lymph vessels join in the thoracic duct and empty into a large neck vein. Others (in the shaded area of the large figure) drain into the right lymph duct. Thus, the fluid, which has been oozing through the walls of the smallest blood vessels into tissue spaces to nourish the cells, returns by itself to the veins entering the heart, to be recirculated by the heart's pumping action.

On its return journey the lymph passes through a hundred or more lymph glands or nodes which act as dams to stop the spread of an infection. When they are overworked, they may swell and become painful. Most of the lymph nodes are tiny, but some, like the tonsils, are large. The largest lymph node of all is the spleen, located in the upper side of the abdomen, which is about the size of a fist.

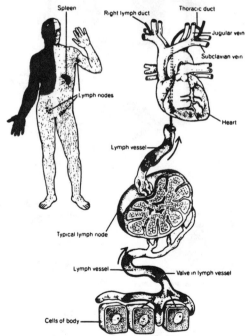

Figure 13-7: The Lymphatic System

Lymphocytes (white cells which fight bacterial infection) are manufactured in the lymph nodes and spleen. To battle invaders, they can squeeze into any tissue in the body and even trickle with the urine from the kidneys into the bladder.

FOR COMMUNICATION:
YOUR BRAIN AND NERVES

The function on the human nervous system is to receive messages from the receptors of the sensory nerves and carry them to the brain and spinal cord. Thus, the effector nerves which spark the processes that sustain life are activated.

Communication between parts of the body is coordinated by a control system with a unit called the neuron which is a single cell usually found bundled into fibers called nerves. The receptors of the sensory nerves (feeling and touch), located everywhere in the body, constantly send information about our environment. Thirty one pairs of spinal nerves carry this information to the spinal cord through the medulla, which is a bulblike enlargement of the spinal cord, into the higher regions of the brain. The brain reacts by way of the effector spinal nerves.

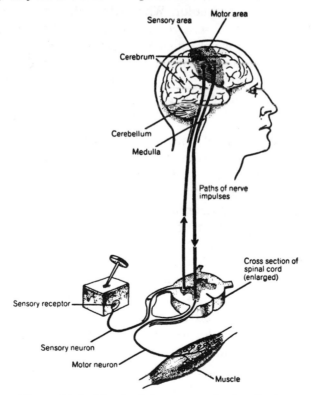

Figure 13-8: The Body's Communication System

Cranial nerves carry information for sight, taste, hearing, smell and other functions to the medulla or directly to other parts of the brain. The medulla also controls such involuntary activities as breathing, digestion and circulation. The cerebrum, comprised of two deeply grooved hemispheres in the brain, controls conscious activities. The cerebellum (underneath and almost covered over) coordinates muscular activities.

THE SPECIAL SENSES:
HEARING, TASTING, SEEING, SMELLING

When stimulated, nerves in the sense organs send impulses to the brain, where they are interpreted. In the innermost layer of the eye, for example, are specialized nerve cells of the retina which are sensitive to light and color. When stimulated, they send sight messages to the brain. Sound waves fathered by the outer ear pass through the auditory canal causing the eardrum to vibrate. Three tiny bones—the hammer, anvil and stirrup on the inner side of the eardrum, relay vibrations to the cochlea, containing the hearing receptor, in the fluid-filled cavity of the inner ear. From there, the acoustic nerve takes the impulses to the brain to be interpreted.

An individual's sense of balance depends on three semicircular canals which lie at right angles to each other in the inner ear. They contain fluid which responds to movements and act as a sort of automatic governor, sending information about body positions to the brain. In addition, numerous sensory nerve endings in muscles, tendons and deep parts of the body inform the brain of the position and state of the body's individual parts. Through nerve communication, an individual can judge the position of an arm or leg even when his eyes are closed.

Taste receptors are located mostly on the tongue, producing sweet, salty, sour or bitter sensations. Smell receptors are chemical-type receptors located at the top of the nasal cavity. They influence smell and taste.

Feeling sensations are detected by different nerve endings, some sensitive to cold and some sensitive to heat. Pain receptors are bare nerve endings in the skin and other organs.

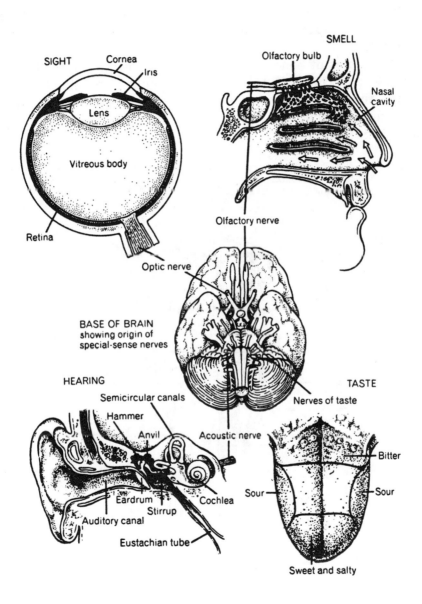

Figure 13-9: The Four Senses

FOR SUPPORT AND MOTION:
YOUR BONES, MUSCLES AND CONNECTIVE TISSUE

Bones give shape to the body, provide a flexible framework to protect vital organs and, with the aid of muscles, enable the body to move.

The centers of bones store red blood cells manufactured by the marrow, particularly in the ribs and vertebrae. Tiny blood vessels course through the tough membrane that covers most bones and pass through each bone in a network of canals. Nerves also reach into the interiors.

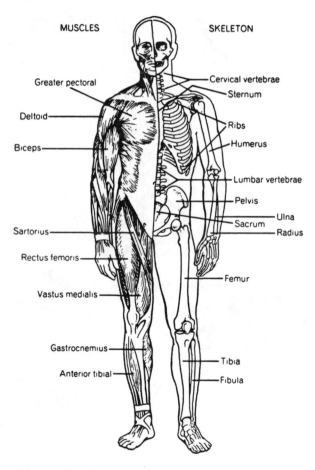

Figure 13-10: The Body's Bones, Muscles and Connective Tissue

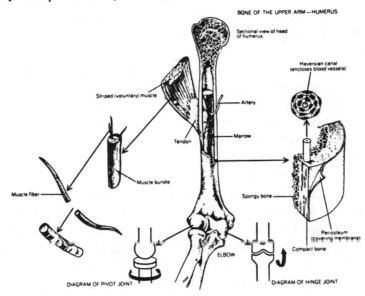

BONE OF THE UPPER ARM—HUMERUS

Sectional view of head of humerus

Haversian canal (encloses blood vessels)

Striped (voluntary) muscle

Artery

Marrow

Tendon

Muscle bundle

Muscle fiber

Spongy bone

Periosteum (covering membrane)

Compact bone

ELBOW

DIAGRAM OF PIVOT JOINT

DIAGRAM OF HINGE JOINT

Figure 13-11: Upper Arm Bone Structure

Each bone (except for the hyoid bone in the throat) meets with another bone at a joint, which may be immovable (like those in the cranium) or movable. The connective tissues which bind bones into a movable framework are called ligaments, tendons or sinews. And to move the body there are over 600 muscles that make up more than half of the body weight.

Muscles that move the skeleton and other parts like the eyes and tongue are called voluntary because they can be moved at will. Others found in the walls of veins and arteries, the intestinal tract and even at the base of the hairs in the skin are involuntary.

The cardiac muscle or heart is an involuntary muscle which has the strength and force of a voluntary muscle.

A mass of cells all performing the same function is called a tissue; several kinds of tissue may be organized to work together and form an organ, such as the liver. A group of organs handling a specific task like circulation or digestion is called a system.

FOR REGULATION:
THE ENDOCRINE GLANDS

Secretions of the endocrine (or ductless) glands are carried by the blood stream to all parts of the body. They affect mental ability, physical strength, reproduction, build, stature, hair growth, voice pitch and behavior. The way people think, act and feel depends largely on these minute secretions in the blood stream.

To maintain normal metabolism, balanced thyroid hormone production is needed. Too little leads to sluggishness; too much to an increased heartbeat, mental activity and oxygen consumption. The pituitary seems to be the master gland producing a large number of hormones, including some that control other glands. One function is to control growth.

The parathyroids regulate the metabolism of important minerals, such as calciums, in the body. The adrenal glands secrete adrenalin and certain other hormones, which step up metabolism and help meet the body's emergencies, as in moments of danger.

Insulin, produced in the pancreas, controls the burning of sugar in the body cells for producing energy. Without enough insulin, diabetes will develop. Gonad is the general term for the male and female sex glands, the testis and the ovary; their hormonal secretions are necessary for conception, reproduction and on individual's maturing.

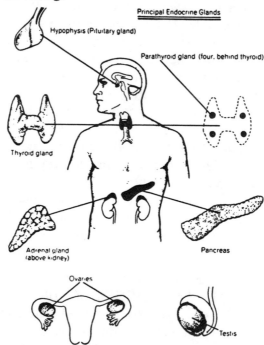

Figure 13-12: The Endrocrine Gland System

FOR TRANSMITTING LIFE:
THE REPRODUCTIVE SYSTEM

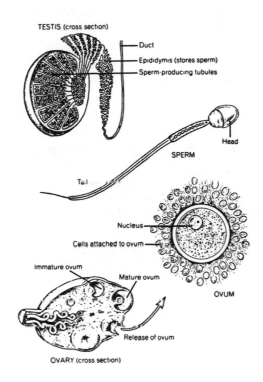

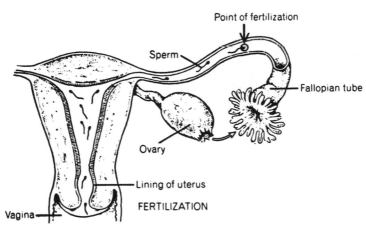

Figure 13-13: The Reproductive System

The ovaries in women and testes in men produce sex cells. Mature egg cells, called ova, are released periodically from the ovary to enter the cavity of the uterus through one of the two Fallopian tubes. Fertilization by a male sperm cell usually takes place in the tube as an ovum encounters a sperm which has traveled up the interior of the uterus. After the two cells have united, the fertilized egg proceeds to the uterus, where it attaches itself to the uterine wall, which is richly lined with nutrient-bearing capillaries.

Tissues from the mother and embryo form the placenta, through which the embryo is fed; wastes, to be eliminated by the mother, are absorbed by it. The growth of a new human being begins.

-----

*Note: These drawings were taken from Harvey's original book of experiments, printed a few years ago in the Scientific American and reproduced here courtesy of the New York Public Library Picture File.

[1]All visual and condensed explanations of the body systems in this section are printed here, courtesy of The Reader's Digest *Great Encyclopedic Dictionary*.

PART FIVE

Simple "Stay Well" Recipes For Everyone At Your House

14

How to Avoid
Medical Expense
All Along the Way

The best way to avoid medical expense is to stay well. Here are the basic requisites for physical and emotional health for seven different age groups.

1. *For Babies Under One Year*
   - Adequate feeding by bottle or breast with relief bottle so mother can have freedom
   - Clean body and clothes
   - Comfortable bed
   - Disease-preventing inoculations
   - Love

2. *For Young Children*
   - Nourishing food

- Comfortable clothes and bed
- Growing self-reliance (encouraged at home and/or at nursery school or Day Care Center)
- Accident prevention
- Relaxed home

3. *For Adolescents*
   - Vitamin-rich diet plus plenty of calcium
   - Adequate sleep
   - Respect for an automobile
   - New areas of self-expression
   - No smoking or drugs

4. *For the Young Married*
   - Nourishing food
   - Individual achievement
   - Proper care of woman during pregnancy and
   - Good driving habits on part of man
   - Balanced exercises and rest
   - Love and respect for each other
   - No smoking

5. *For the Middle-aged Male*
   - No smoking
   - Sensible exercise
   - Low cholesterol diet
   - Feeling of worth
   - Active sex life

6. *For the Middle-aged Female*
   - No smoking

- Hormones during menopause
- Low cholesterol diet
- Exercise
- Feeling of worth

7. *For the Over-65*
- No smoking
- Sensible exercise
- Good food
- Lack of loneliness
- Variety of interests

Read through the recipes and you will find few calls for medicines and/or drugs. There's a reason. Medicines are prescribed as a supplement for what nature provides or as a corrective measure. With good health,[1] neither is necessary.

[1]If you have a handicap or a chronic physical disability, define good health as it applies to you personally. Are you functioning each day at your optimum within your *personal*, physical and mental framework? If so, you are healthy in the context of this book.

15

Health Robbers
to be Avoided
All Along the Way

Certain health problems threaten some age groups more than others. Here is the list of dangers.

1. *Infants*
   - Diarrhea
   - Dehydration
   - Colds and middle ear infections
   - Malnutrition
   - Falls

2. *Children*
   - Colds and their after-effects
   - Streptococcus infections
   - Accidents
   - Meningitis
   - Malnutrition

3. *Adolescents*
- Emotional disturbances
- Accidents
- Skin problems
- Drugs
- Malnutrition

4. *Young Married People*
- Emotional problems
- Problems connected with pregnancy
- Accidents
- Alcoholism and/or drug problems
- Anemia
- Headaches

5. *Middle-aged Men*
- Heart trouble
- Hypertension
- Ulcers
- Prostate trouble
- Alcoholism
- Cancer

6. *Middle-aged Women*
- Menopausal problems
- Hypertension
- Cancer
- Headaches
- Thyroid problems
- Alcoholism

7. *The Over-65*
- Falls
- Strokes
- Diabetes
- Heart attacks
- Arthritis

Respecting the susceptibility of your age group to specific problems can help you to guard against these problems. This does not mean that you will worry about everything that might happen, but it does mean that you will not tempt fate. As a middle-aged man, you will not let yourself go to flab, smoke heavily and/or forget exercise. And as a middle-aged woman, you won't neglect a lump in your breast. When you know what to watch for, you can save money and, in some cases, your life.

16

Three Vital D's That Make for Well-Being: Diet, Deep-Breathing and Delight in Life

An over-supply of mushy material containing cholesterol in the arteries of both men and women is a health hazard that may start with poor eating habits early in life. In the middle years, the condition is aggravated by overweight, lack of exercise, high blood pressure, cigarette smoking and the wear and tear of age, but none of these is the real villain. A lifetime of wrong eating may be primary cause of arteriosclerosis, which in turn causes heart attacks, but some suspect other causes. Research continues.

The build-up of cholesterol goes along slowly through the years until deposits (like deposits of lime in a water pipe) gradually coat the interior walls of the arteries until no blood can get through. Unfortunately, a taste for starchy, high fat foods has become pronounced by the time the condition is a problem. Then, a switch in eating habits is difficult.

We can't advise you to go on a crash diet which contains no sugar, salt, starch and fat in order to avoid trouble later on. It won't work. But what we can suggest for the good of you and your family is that you cut down on cooking with fat (or eating fatty foods) day by day by day. Next time you shop, buy fish or chicken instead of high-fat meat; margarine instead of butter; fruit instead of pastry. Don't keep solid shortening in the house, and cook with oil, only. Gradually, your eating habits will change, and those around you will be better off because of this.

IF YOU ARE OVERWEIGHT

If you are carrying around extra pounds, you can be sure you have deposits of hard fat all through your body (3,500 calories for a single pound of unused fat). To get rid of this fat you have to use it up, and that means exercising more and eating less, so that by expending more energy you can absorb the banked deposits. The only way to do this is to consume fewer new calories than you have been consuming.

Don't aim for a quick take-off of fat deposits that have been building up for years, but do cut out fats and pastries (which are made with saturated fats) and the deposits will gradually go. Just as fatty places in your body can disappear so can the *unseen fatty deposits in your arteries.*

DEEP-BREATHING

One of the sure-fire ways to spot a high coronary risk during a heart examination is with the "vital capacity test" given in clinics like Preventive Medicine Institute, Strang Clinic in New York City. There, the amount of air a man or woman takes into the lungs during normal inhaling is measured when it is expelled. A low intake means a high coronary risk; a large intake means a low risk. The reason is obvious: a skimpy amount of air coming into the lungs means that too little oxygen is being absorbed into the blood; thus, blood quality is bound to be diminished.

To increase your oxygen intake, practice abdominal breathing. Lie flat to begin with (although, later, you can do this breathing exercise as you sit, stand and walk). Consciously, fill your abdomen area with air, letting your stomach expand like a balloon. Continue inhaling, feeling your chest expand as your lungs fill. Finally, let the expansion continue into the windpipe and neck region. In the beginning, breathe in through the nose (filling the abdomen, chest and neck region in that order) as you count slowly to four. Hold your breath while you count to eight.

Then, exhale through the mouth as you count to six. Next day, make your aim in five, hold ten, out seven. Do not strain, but gradually breathe deeper, expanding your abdomen and lungs as you progress to: in five, hold 20, out ten. This deep-breathing plan gives you a vitality-boosting diet of oxygen.

DELIGHT IN LIFE

A few years ago, Dr. George Gallup in Princeton, surveyed a large cross-section of men and women over 75 years old who were happy and active in their way of life. He found no magic elixir that accounted for each one's longevity but he did find that all had one characteristic in common. *They were interested in everything!*

His conclusion: men and women who want to live to an active old age should cultivate a *delight in life.*

At whatever stage of living that you find yourself, and however old your other family members may be, begin today to concentrate on the 3 Ds—*diet, deep-breathing* and *delight in life* for you and for them. Your family medical bills are bound to go down and life will be more enjoyable for all of you for years to come.

BIBLIOGRAPHY

Blakeslee, Alton and Stamler, Dr. Jeremiah *Your Heart Has Nine Lives,* Prentice-Hall, Inc., New Jersey

Bolton, Dr. William *What to do Until the Doctor Comes,* The Reilly & Lee Co., Chicago, 1953

Boy Scouts of America *Boy Scout Handbook,* New Brunswick, New Jersey, February, 1970, 6th printing

Burack, Dr. Richard *The Handbook of Prescription Drugs, Official Names, Prices and Sources for Patient and Doctor,* Pantheon Books, A Division of Random House, New York, 1967

Crohn, Dr. Burrill Bernard *An Oral History,* The American Gastroenterological Association, Wilmington, Delaware, 1968

Davis, Adelle *Let's Eat Right to Keep Fit,* Harcourt, Brace & Co., New York, 1954

Editors of Consumer Reports *The Medicine Show,* Consumers Union, Mount Vernon, New York, Revised 1963 Edition

Encyclopedia Britannica, Volume 11, William Benton Publisher, 1955 Printing

Encyclopedia Britannica, Volume 15, William Benton Publisher, 1955 Printing

Fishbein, Dr. Morris *The Handy Home Medical Advisor and Concise Medical Encyclopedia,* Revised Edition, Doubleday & Co., Garden City, New York, 1963

Furnas, J. C. *The Americans,* A Social History of the United States, 1587-1914, G. P. Putnam's Sons, New York, 1969

Gomez, Dr. Joan, edited by Dr. Marvin J. Gersh *A Dictionary of Symptoms,* Stein and Day Publishers, New York, 1967

Goodman, Louis S., Gilman, Alfred *The Pharmacological Basis of Therapeutics,* Third Edition, The Macmillan Company, New York

Gould, Dr. George M. *A Pocket Medical Dictionary,* 8th Edition, Revised, P. Blakiston's Son & Co., Philadelphia, Pa.

Harrison, T. R. *Principles of Internal Medicine,* Fifth Edition, McGraw-Hill Book Co., New York

Kinney, Jean and Cle *How to Get 20 to 90% Off On Everything You Buy,* Parker Publishing Company, West Nyack, New York, 1966

Lingeman, Richard R. *Drugs from A to Z: A Dictionary,* McGraw-Hill Book Company, New York, 1969

MD Publications, Inc., *MD Medical Newsmagazine,* New York, Vol. 7, No. 7, July 1963

Miller, Dr. Benjamin F. *The Complete Medical Guide,* Revised, Simon and Schuster, New York, 1967

Moyer, Carl A.; Rhoads, Jonathan E.; Allen, J. Garrott; Harkins, Henry N. *Surgery, Principles and Practice,* J. B. Lippincott Co., Philadelphia, Pa.

National Organizations of the United States *Encyclopedia of Associations,* Volume 1, 5th Edition, Gale Research Company, Detroit, Mich., 48226

Nelson, Waldo E.; Vaughan, Victor C.; McKay, James R. *Textbook of Pediatrics,* 9th Edition, W. B. Saunders Co., Philadelphia, Pa., 1969

Reilley, Harold J. *The Secret of Better Health,* Carlyle House, New York, 1941

Schindler, Dr. John A. *How to Live 365 Days a Year,* Fawcett Publications, Inc., Greenwich, Conn. (Reprinted by arrangement with Prentice-Hall, Inc.), 1954

Scientific American, New York, N. Y., June 1952

Silverman, Milton *Magic in a Bottle,* The Macmillan Company, New York, 1951

Snively, Dr. William D., Jr., with Thuerbach, Jan *Sea of Life,* David McKay Company, Inc., New York, 1969

The American National Red Cross *First Aid,* 4th Edition, Doubleday and Co., Inc., Garden City, New York, 1969

The American National Red Cross *Red Cross Home Nursing Textbook,* The Blakiston Co., Philadelphia, Pa., 1950

The Basic Everyday Encyclopedia, Random House, New York, 1954

The Random House Dictionary of the English Language, The Unabridged Edition, Jess Stein, Editor-in-Chief, Random house, New York, 1966

The Reader's Digest *Great Encyclopedic Dictionary,* Pleasantville, New York, 1968

Thompson, Ella M. and LeBaron, Margaret *Simplified Nursing, The Essentials of Practical Nursing,* J. B. Lippincott Company, Philadelphia, Pa., 1960

Today's Health Guide, Edited by Dr. W. W. Bauer, American Medical Association, 1965

Index

A

AAA, 192
Abdominal trouble, 62, 108-109
Accidents:
    coverage, 191-193
    driving, 88
    prevention, associations, 206
    principal types, 109-116
Acetylsalicylic acid, 26
Acne, 25, 96
Addicts Anonymous, 211
Addison's disease, 116
Adenoids, enlarged, 82-83
Adhesive bandages:
    bee sting, 31
    buy for less, 31
    minor scrape or cut, 30-31
    not tinted with medicine, 30
    perforated, 30
    purpose, 30
    second degree burn, 31
    uses, 30-31
    warnings, 30
Adolescents:
    acne, 96
    acute heart attack, 105
    alcohol, 96
    alcoholic stupor, 106
    allergies, 96-97
    anemia, 97
    artificial respiration, 95
    broken leg or other fracture, 91
    cavities, 97
    cramps while swimming, 97
    dandruff, 97
    dangers, 240
    excess fat, 98
    eyestrain, 98
    diabetes, 98

Adolescents *(Cont'd)*
    diabetic coma, 105
    drugs, 96
    emotional problems, 104
    epileptic attack, 106
    fainting spell, 106
    fractured neck or back, 90-91
    freezing to death, 106
    goiter, 98-99
    gonorrhea, 99
    homosexuality, 99
    malnutrition, 99
    masturbation, 100
    menstrual abnormalities, 100
    mononucleosis, 100
    mouth-to-mouth breathing, 94-95
    near drowning, 90
    neurotic symptoms, 100
    nocturnal emissions (wet dreams), 101
    oily hair and skin, 101
    overdose of sleeping pills, 106
    perspiration odor, 101
    poison, 93-94
    poisonous snake bite, 91-93
    posture, 101
    requisites for physical and emotional
      health, 236
    rheumatoid arthritis, 101-102
    schizophrenia, 102
    sexual promiscuity, 102
    smoking, 103
    spurting blood, 93
    stricken, unable to talk, 105-106
    stroke, 105
    sunstroke, 106
    tuberculosis, 103
    tularemia, 103
    underweight, 104
    undeveloped sex organs, 103

Advertising, 46, 48
Aged, associations, 206
Air pollution, 198
Alcohol, 96
Alcoholic stupor, 106
Alcoholism, 116, 206-207
Allergic rhinitis, antihistamine tablets, 31-32
Allergies, 96-97
American Medical Associations, 209
Aminophylline, U.S.P., 40
Amputation, 116
Anemia, 40, 97, 116-117
Aneurysm, 117
Angina pectoris, nitroglycerin, U.S.P., 41
Antacid:
    bicarbonate of soda, 29-30
    milk of magnesia, 28
Antibiotic, 43
Antihistamine tablets:
    allergic rhinitis, 31-32
    children, doctor's recommendation, 31
    chlorpheniramine Maleate, U.S.P., 32
    cold symptoms, 32
    definition, 31
    Diphenhydramine Hydrochloride,
        U.S.P., 32
    drowsiness, 31, 32
    hay fever symptoms, 31
    side effects, 32
    warnings, 31
Anxiety, 41, 86
Appendicitis, 108, 117-118
Appetite suppressant, 39
Arteries, hardening, 118-119
Arteriosclerosis, 118-119
Arthritis, 27, 42, 101-102, 119
Arthritis Foundation, 200
Artificial respiration, 95
Asphyxia, 62, 120
Aspirin:
    acetylsalicylic acid, 26
    allergy to it, 27
    buffering with bicarbonate of soda, 27
    buy for less, 27
    decomposition, 27-28
    discount drug store, 27
    "glorified," 27
    label, 27
    pain reliever, 27
    reduce fever, 26
    relieve cold symptoms, 26
    size of supply, 27
    suppress inflammation in arthritic
        joints, 27
    upsetting to stomach, 27
        use, 26-27

Aspirin *(Cont'd)*
    with plenty of water, 27
    wonder drug, 26
Associations, sources of free medical
    information, 205-212
Asthma, 40, 120, 207
Athlete's Foot, 141-142
Attitude, 176, 245
Audiology and Speech Correction
    Center, 211
Aureomycin, 43

B

Baby *(see also* Child):
    bites, 55
    chafed skin, 57
    chapped skin, 57
    colds, coughs, croup, stuffy nose, 56
    colic, 56
    constipation, 56
    crossed eyes, strobismus, 57
    dangers, 239
    diaper rash, 58
    dry skin, 58
    fever, 57
    first year, 53-55
    hiccups, 57
    impetigo, 58
    jaundice, 57
    prickly heat, 58
    reflexes, 54
    requisites for physical and emotional
        health, 235
    ringworm of scalp, 58
    scratches or minor cuts, 57
    silver nitrate, 53
    spitting up, 58
    stuck eyelids, 58
    swallowing object, 58, 81-82
    teething, 59
    weaning, 59
    winter itch, 58
Bacitracin Neomycin, 58
Backache, 121
Baldness, 121
Bandages, adhesive, 30-31
Barber's itch, 121
Bed-wetting, 71
Bee sting, bandage, 31
Belladonna Tincture, U.S.P., 38-39
Bicarbonate of soda:
    antacid, 29-30
    "buffers" aspirin, 30
    check perspiration, 30

Bicarbonate of soda *(Cont'd)*
    clean teeth, 30
    definition, 29
    first degree burns, 29
    hives, 30
    insect bites, 30
    itching caused by allergy, 30
    uses, 29-30
Birth defects, association, 207
Birthmark, 67
Bites:
    chigger and mosquito, 55
    poisonous insect, 61
Bladder trouble, 121-122
Blindness, associations, 198, 207-208 (*see also* Eyes)
Blood:
    circulation, 213
    loss, 173
    pressure, 43
    spurting, 93
    stool, 62, 68
    urine, 62, 68
    vessels, explanation, 222-223
    vomit, 68
Blow on head, child, 63
Blue Cross and Blue Shield, 192
Body:
    blood vessels and heart, 222-223
    bones, muscles, connective tissue, 228-229
    brain and nerves, 225-226
    digestive system, 219
    endocrine glands, 229-230
    hearing, tasting, seeing, smelling, 226-227
    lymphatic system, 223-224
    reproductive system, 231-232
    respiratory system, 221-222
    skin, 217-218
    urinary system, 220
Boils, 122
Bones:
    broken, 64-65
    explanation, 228-229
Brain:
    explanation, 225-226
    tumor, 122-123
Brain Research Foundation, 208
Breast, lump, 123, 125
Breathing, deep-, 244-245
Breathlessness, 123-124
Bronchopneumonia, child, 68
Burack, Richard, 40
Burns:
    bandage, 31
    chemical, 112

Burns *(Cont'd)*
    first degree, bicarbonate of soda, 29
    hot water, 124
    thermal, 112
    third degree, 174
Bursitis, 124
Buxom Bells, International, 211

C

Cancer, 108, 109, 125-126, 199, 208
Cancer Society, 198
Car sickness, 68, 154
Cataracts, 126
Cauliflower ears, 126
Cavities, 97, 168-169
Cerebral palsy, associations, 200, 208
Cervicitis, 126-127
Chafed skin, baby, 57
Chancroid, 127
Chapped skin, baby, 57
Chicken pox, 68-69
Chiggers, baby, 55
Child:
    abdominal trouble, 62
    adolescent, 89-106 (see also Adolescence)
    asphyxiation, 62, 63
    baby, 33-59 (see also Baby)
    bed-wetting, 71
    birthmark, 67
    bitten by poisonous insect, 61
    broken bone, 64-65
    bronchopneumonia, 68
    car sickness, 68
    chicken pox, 68-69
    choking, 61
    chronically ill, 200
    convulsion, 62
    crippled, 200, 210
    cystitis, 68
    dangers, 239
    deep cuts, 61
    diarrhea, 62, 69
    diphtheria, 69
    dog bite, 69
    drowning, 61, 63
    ear problems, 62, 70
    eczema, 70
    electric shock, 61, 63
    emotional disturbances, 70-71
    epilepsy, 62
    exhaustion from heat, 61
    eye problems, 71-73
    fainting, 61, 63
    fall, 61, 63

Child *(Cont'd)*
  fat, 83
  feces, blood in, 62, 68
  fever, 62
  food allergy, 73-74
  foreign object in air or food passage, 63
  head blow, 63
  head lice, 74
  headrolling, rocking or banging, 71
  heart murmur, 74
  hernia, 74
  high, sharp, screaming cry, 62
  influenza, 75
  loss of consciousness, 61-62
  low, moaning cry, 62
  masturbation, 71
  measles, 75
  meningitis, 62, 75-76
  moles, 67
  nephritis, 68
  nervous hacking cough, 62
  over-anxious parent, 86
  poison ivy, 76-77
  poisoned, 61, 63, 77-79 (*see also* Poison)
  rash, 62
  rectal polyp or fissure, 68
  requisites for physical and emotional
        health, 235-236
  rheumatic fever, 79
  roseola infantum, 79
  scarlet fever, 79
  scurvy, 68
  sebaceous cysts, 67
  serious illness, 61-63
  sinusitis, 79
  smashed finger, 80
  smegma, 80
  stomach-ache, 80
  "strawberry marks," 67
  Streptococcus infection, 80
  stuttering, 71
  sudden trouble, 61-65
  sunburn, 81
  swallowing object, 58, 81-82
  swollen glands, 82
  thin, 83-84
  thrush, 82
  thumb-sucking, 71
  tonsillitis or enlarged adenoids, 82-83
  tooth decay, 84
  tumor, 68
  ulcer, 68
  urine, blood in, 62, 68
  vomit, blood in, 68
  vomiting, 62, 84-85
  warts, 85
    whooping cough, 85

Child *(Cont'd)*
  worms, 85-86
  worrisome problems, 67-88
  wound needing stitches, 62
Child Care, associations, 208
Childbirth and/or childbirth complications,
      128-130
Children American Association of
      Psychiatric Clinics, 210
Children's Bureau, 210
Chlorpheniramine Maleate, U.S.P., 32
Chlortetracycline hydrochloride, N.F., 43
Choking spell, 61, 130
Cholera, 130
  Chronic diseases, associations, 208
Chronic problem, 183-185
Chronically ill child, 200
Circulation, blood, 213
Circulatory problems, 130-131
Cirrhosis, 116, 151-152
Cleft Palate Association, American, 208
Cold sore, 132
Colds:
  antihistamine tablets, 32
  aspirin, 26
  baby, 56
  symptoms, cause, treatment, 131-132
Colic, baby, 56
Colitis, 108, 131
Comeback, Inc., 211
Commercials, 48
Congestion, nasal, 41-42
Connective tissue, explanation, 228-229
Consciousness, loss, 61
Constipation, 29, 56, 132-133
Contraceptives, 42
Convulsion, child, 62
Coronary, 130-133
Coughs:
  baby, 56
  child, 62
  smoker's, 134
Cramps, 97
Crippled child, 200
Crippling diseases, associations, 208
Crossed eyes, baby, 57
Croup, baby, 56
Crying, child, 62
Cuts, 57, 61
Cyst, 67
Cyst, tailbone, 134
Cystic Fibrosis Research Foundation,
      National, 209
Cystitis, 68

                    D

Dandruff, 25, 97

Deafness, 70, 134-135, 209
Decavitamin capsules (or tablets), U.S.P., 39
Deductions, tax 191, 193
Deep-breathing, 244-245
Delight, 245
Delirium tremens, 137-138
Department of Health, Education and Welfare, 198, 199
Department of Health, town, 197
Dextroamphetamine sulfate, U.S.P., 39
Diabetes, 41, 98, 135, 198, 199
Diabetes Association, American, 209
Diabetes Foundation, 209
Diabetic coma, 105
Diagnostic services, free, 198-199
Diaper rash, baby, 58
Diarrhea, 41, 62, 69, 136
Diet, 244
Dietetic Association, American, 211
Diethylstilbesterol, U.S.P., 39
Digestive system, explanation, 219
Digitalis, U.S.P., 39-40
Dimenhydrinate, 40
Diphenhydramine hydrochloride, U.S.P., 32, 40
Diphtheria, child, 69
Disc, slipped, 137
Disfigurement, 136-137
Diuretic, 43
Doctor:
    appointment, 189-191
    asking for generic drug, 47
    drugs prescribed, 35-44
    "family medical diary," 191
    house-call, 191
    prescription, 36-38
    reasons to consult, 38
    subject to advertising techniques, 46, 48
Dog bite, 69
Dowager's hump, 138
Dramamine, 40
Dreser, Hermann, 26
Driver, rules, 88
Drowning, near, 61, 63, 90, 112-113
Drug addiction, 96
Dry skin, baby, 58
Dysentery, 138-139

E

Earache, child, 62, 70
Ears, cauliflower, 126
Eczema, 70, 139
Elderly, 237, 240
Electric shock, child, 61, 63

Emergencies, preparation, 49-50
Emotional and physical health, requisites, 235-237
Emotional disturbances, child, 70-71
Emphysema, 139,198
Emphysema and Chronic Bronchitis, Task Force, 209
Emphysema Anonymous, 209
Encephalitis, 165, 199
Endocrine glands, explanation, 229-230
Entrusil, 37
Ephedrine sulfate, U.S.P., 40
Epilepsy, 62, 139
Epilepsy Foundation of America, 209
Epileptic attack, 106
Estrogen, 42
Examination, 184, 187-188, 198, 199
Exhaustion from heat, child, 61
Eyes:
    crossed, 57
    lids stuck, 58
    loss of sight, 140
    problems, children, 71-73
    spots, 140
    strain, 98

F

Fainting, 61, 63, 98, 106
Falls, 61, 110-112, 140
"Family medical diary," 191
Fat, 83-84, 98, 157, 244
Female, middle-aged, 236-237, 240
Femoral hernia, 146-147
Ferrous sulfate, U.S.P., 40
Fever:
    aspirin, 26
    baby, 57
    child, 62
Finger, smashed, 80
Fissure, rectal, 162
Fitness programs, 188-189
Florence Crittenton Homes Association, 212
Flu, 75, 108, 141
Food allergy, 73-74
Food and Nutrition Board, 211
Food poisoning, 108, 141
Foot trouble, 141-142
Foundations, 199-200
Fracture:
    leg, 91
    neck or back, 90-91
Free medical information sources, 205-212

Free services:
    crippled or chronic disease, 200
    diagnostic, 198-199
    foundations, 199-200
    government wants you to have, 199
    if you can afford to pay, 198
    more help than you know, 201
    Visiting Nurse Association, 197, 200-201
Freezing to death, 106
"Functional" disease, 185

G

Gall bladder, 109, 142
Gantrisin, 37
Gases, 115
General practitioner, 190
Generic names, 23-24, 34, 35-44, 45, 47
Georgia Warm Springs Foundation, 200,
    210
German measles, 75
Glaucoma, 142-143, 198, 199
Glycerin suppositories, 29
Goiter, 98-99
Gonorrhea, 99
Gout, 143
Government, 199
Gray hair, 143
Griseofulvin, U.S.P., 58
Gunshot wound, 113

H

Hair, gray, 143
"Handbook of Prescription Drugs," 40
Hangover, 143-144
Happiness, 245
Hardening of the arteries, 118-119
Harvest mites, 55
Harvey, William 213
Hay fever, 31, 144
Head blow, child, 63
Head lice, 74
Headache:
    migraine, 144
    tension, 144-145
Headrolling, rocking and banging, 71
Health Council, National, 209
Health Coverage, 187-188, 191-193
Health Foundations, United, 209
Health Organizations, 209
Hearing:
    associations, 209
    explanation, 226-227

Heart *(Cont'd)*
    attack, 105
    disorder, 145-146
    explanation, 222-223
    massage, 177
    murmur, 74
Heart Association, American, 209
Heart Information Center, 209
Heartburn, 145
Heat exhaustion, child, 61
Hemophilia Foundation, National, 209
Hemorrhoids, 146
Hepatitis, 146
Hernia:
    femoral, 146-147
    inguinal, 146-147
    umbilical, 74, 146-147
Herpes simplex, 132
Herpes Zoster, 164
Hiccups, baby, 57
High blood pressure, 43
Hiking clubs, 189
Hip:
    congenital dislocated, 147
    fractured, 147
Hives, bicarbonate of soda, 30
Hoarseness, 148
Homosexuality, 99
Hookworm, 85
Hospitalization policy, 187-188, 191-193
Hot water burns, 124
Hump, 138
Hydrocortisone ointment, U.S.P., 40-41
Hypertension, 43
Hysterectomy, 148

I

Illegitimacy, National Council, 212
Impetigo, 58
Indigestion, 148-149
Infantile Paralysis, 210
Infantile Paralysis, National Foundation,
    200
Influenza, 75, 108, 141
Information sources, medical, free, 205-
    212
Inguinal hernia, 146-147
Insect bite, 30, 61
Insomnia, 149
Insulin injection, U.S.P., 41
Insurance policies, list, 192

Intercourse, painful, 149-150
Internal poisons, 115-116
Intestinal flu, 108
Iron deficiency, 40
Itch, winter, 58
Itching, rectal, 162

J

Jaundice, 57, 150

K

Kidney Foundation, National, 210
Kidney problems, 150

L

Laryngitis, 150-151
Laxative, milk of magnesia, 28
Lead poisoning, 198-199
Leprosy, 151
Leprosy, Leonard Wood Memorial for
    Eradication, 210
Leukemia Society of America, 210
Leukorrea, 151
Lice, 74
Life insurance, 187-188, 191-193
Lockjaw, 152
Long-term disease, 183-185
Lumbago, 152
Lump in breast, 123, 125
Lymphatic system explanation, 223-224

M

Machinery, 115
Malnutrition, 99
Male, middle-aged, 236, 240
Margaret Sanger Research Foundation,
    212
Married people, young, 236, 240
Massage, heart, 177
Mastoid, child, 70
Masturbation, 71, 100
Maternal and Child Health, American
    Association, 210
Maternity Center Association, 210
Measles, 75
Medic-Alert Foundation International,
    209
Medicaid, 193

Medical Association, American, 209
"Medical diary," 191
Medical information sources, free, 205-212
Medical Research, National Society, 210
Medicare, 192, 193, 199
Men, middle-aged, 236, 240
Meniere's disease, 152
Meningitis, 62, 75-76
Menopausal problems, 39, 152-153
Menstrual abnormalities, 100
Mental attitude, 176, 245
Mental Health Foundation, American, 210
Mental Health, National Association, 210
Mental problems, 153-154
Mentally Ill Children, Association for, 210
Metahydrin, 43
Middle-age, 236-237, 240
Migraine headache, 144
Milk of magnesia:
    antacid, 28
    avoid habitual use, 28
    definition, 28
    generic name, 28-29
    laxative, 28
    liquid, 28
    save money, 28-29
    uses, 28
Miscarriage, 109, 160
Moles, dark brown, 67
Mononucleosis, 100
Mosquitos, 55
Motion sickness, 68, 154
Motor vehicle accident, 109-110
Mouth-to-mouth breathing, 94-95
Multiple sclerosis, 154
Multiple Sclerosis Society, 200, 210
Muscles, explanation, 228-229
Muscular dystrophy, 154
Muscular Dystrophy Associations of
    America, 210
Myasthenia Gravis Foundation, 210

N

Narcotic Education, International
    Federation, 211
Narcotics Education, 211
Narcotics, National Association for
    Prevention, 211
Nasal congestion, 41-42

National associations, sources of free
    medical information, 205-212
Nausea, 40
Neck, stiff, 154-155, 173
Neo-synephrine, 42
Nephritis, 68
Nerves:
    explanation, 225-226
    impaired, 155
Nervous tension, 155-156
Neuritis, 156-157
Neuromuscular Diseases, National
    Foundation, 211
Neuroses, 156
Neurotic symptoms, 100
Nitroglycerin, U.S.P., 41
Nocturnal emissions, 101
Nose drops, 41-42
Nose, stuffy, 56
Numbness, 157
Nutrition, associations, 211

O

Obesity, 83-84, 98, 157, 244
Oily skin and hair, 101
Organizations, sources of free medical
    information, 205-212
Osteoarthritis, 119
Overweight, 244
Oxygen, insufficient, 174
Oxytetracycline, N.F., 43

P

Pain, aspirin, 27
Pancreas, malfunction, 157-158
Pap test, 125, 198, 199
Paralysis, 158
Paraplegia Foundation, National, 211
Paregoric, U.S.P., 41
Parents:
    over-anxious, 86
    unmarried, 212
Parkinson's Disease, 158-159
Parkinson's Disease Foundation, 211
Pediculosis, 159
Penicillin, 42
People-to-People Health Foundation, 209
Peptic ulcer, 169-170
Pernicious anemia, 117
Perspiration odor, 30, 101

Petrolatum, U.S.P., 58
Pharmacist, 49
Phenobarbitol, U.S.P., 41
Phenylephrine hydrochloride, U.S.P.,
    41-42
Physical and emotional health,
    requisites, 235-237
Physical examinations (see Examinations)
Physical fitness programs, 188-189
Physical Medicine and Rehabilitation,
    Institute, 212
Physical therapy, 185
Pinworms, 86
Pituitary Agency, National, 211
Planned Parenthood - World
    Population, 212
Pleurisy, 68, 159
Pneumonia, 68, 159-160
Poison ivy, 76-77
Poisons:
    adolescents, 93-94
    ammonia, 77
    arsenic, 78
    aspirins, 61, 79, 93-94
    bleach, 77
    carbolic acid, 77
    child, 61, 63, 77-79
    crayons, 77, 78
    detergent, 77
    drain cleaner, 77
    external, 174
    food, 93-94, 108, 141
    gases, 115
    internal, 115-116, 174
    kerosene, 63, 77
    lye, 77
    moth-balls, 77
    paint, 78
    polish, 77
    scouring powder, 77
    silver, 77
    sleeping pills, 93-94, 106
Polyp, 109
Post nasal drip, 160-161
Posture, poor, 101
Potassium penicillin G tablets, U.S.P.
    (buffered), 42
Prednisone, U.S.P., 42
Pregnancy complications, 160
Prescription, 36-38
Prickly heat, baby, 58

Progesterone, 42
Prostate trouble, 161
Psoriasis, 161
Psychiatric Association, American, 210
Psychiatric Clinics for Children,
    American Association, 210
Psychiatrist, 185
Psychologist, 185
Psychoses, 156
Psychosomatic disease, 185
Public Affairs Committee, 212
Public Health Department, 198
Publicity, 46, 48
Pyorrhea, 161-162

Q

Quinsy, 162

R

Radiation, 124
Rash, child, 62
Recreation, 188-189
Rectal fissure, 162
Rectal itching, 162
Red Cross, American National, 209
Redbugs, 55
Reducing, associations, 211
Rehabilitation Centers, Association, 211
Rehabilitation Association, National, 211
Rehabilitation Committee, American, 211
Rehabilitation Foundation, American, 211
Rehabilitation Institute of Physical
    Medicine and, 212
Reproductive system, explanation, 231-232
Researching, 205
Reserpine, U.S.P., 43
Respiration, 94-95
Respiratory system, explanation, 221-222
Retarded Children, Association for
    Help of, 212
Retarded Children, National Association
    for, 212
Retarded Infants Services, Inc., 212
Rheumatic fever, 79
Rheumatoid arthritis, 101, 119
Rhinitis, allergic, 31-32
Ringworm of scalp, baby, 59
Roseola infantum, 79
Roundworms, 86
Rubella, 75
Rubeola, 75

S

Sarcoidosis, 163
Scarlet fever, 79
Schizophrenia, 102
Sciatica, 163
Scratches, baby, 57
Screaming, child, 62
Scurvy, 68
"Seat worms," 86
Sebaceous cysts, 67
Sedative, phenobarbitol, 41
Seeing, explanation, 226-227
Senses, 226-227
Services, free (*see* Free services)
Sex Information and Education Council
    of U.S., 212
Sex organs, undeveloped, 103
Sexual maladjustment, 163
Sexual promiscuity, 102
Shaking palsy, 158-159
Shingles, 164
Shock, 173, 174
Shoulder, frozen, 164
Sight, associations, 207-208
Silver nitrate, 53
Sinusitis, 79, 165
Sixty-five years, over, 237, 240
Skin:
    explanation, 217-218
    problems, 40-41, 57-58, 164
    (*see also* Baby)
Sleeping pills:
    phenobarbitol, 41
    poison, 93-94, 106
Sleeping sickness, 165
Slipped disc, 137
Smashed finger, 80
Smegma, 80
Smelling:
    explanation, 226-227
Smoking, 103, 134
Snake bite, 91-93
Soap:
    antiseptic, 24
    floating, 25
    how it works, 24
    least possible money, 25-26
    lubricant, 25
    medicated, 25-26
    prevent intake of germs, 25
    rid skin of acne, 25
    uses, 24-25
    wash away dandruff flakes, 25
Social Health Association, American, 212

Social security, 193
Sore throat, 165-166
Special services, tax-supported, 197-204
    (*see also* Free services)
Specialist, 190
Speech Correction Center, Audiology
    and, 211
Speech, loss, 105-106
Spitting up, 58
Staphylococcus, penicillin, 42
Sterility, 212
Stitches, wound needing, 62
Stiff neck, 154-155
Stomach:
    ache, 80
    mixing ingredients, 48-49
Stool, blood in, 62, 68
Strabismus, baby, 57
"Strawberry marks," 67
Streptococcus infection, 42, 80
Stroke, 105, 166
Stuffy nose, baby, 56
Stuttering, 71
Sulfisoxazole, 37, 43
Sunburn, 81, 166-167
Sunstroke, 106
Suppositories, glycerin, 29
Swallowing objects:
    sharp, 81-82
    smooth, 58
Swollen glands, child, 82
Syphilis, 167-168, 198, 199
"Systems," body, 217-232
    (*see also* Body)

T

Tailbone cyst, 134
Tasting, explanation, 226-227
Tax deductions, 191, 193
Tax-supported special services, 197-204
    (*see also* Free services)
Teeth:
    bicarbonate of soda, 30
    cavities, 97
    permanent, loss, 168-169
Teething, 59
Tension headache, 144
Terramycin, 43
Tetanus booster, 57
Tetracycline hydrochloride, U.S.P., 43
Therapy, physical, 185
Thiazides, 43
Thin, too, 83-84
Thrush, 82
Thumb-sucking, 71
Thyroid trouble, 169
Tic douloureux, 137

Tonsillitis, 82-83
Tooth decay, 84, 97
Tops Club, 211
Tranquilizer, phenobarbitol, 41
Traveling, 49, 170-171
Tuberculosis, 68, 103, 198, 199
Tuberculosis and Respiratory Disease
    Association, National, 212
Tularemia, 103
Tumor, brain, 122-123
T. V. commercials, 48

U

Ulcer, 108, 169-170
Umbilical hernia, 74, 146-147
Underweight, 83-84, 104
United Health Foundations, 209
Unmarried mothers, 212
Unmarried Parents, National Association
    on Service to, 212
Urinalysis, free, 198, 199
Urinary system, explanation, 220
Urinary tract infection, 43
Urine, blood in, 62, 68
Uterus, displaced, 170

V

Vaccinations before traveling, 170-171
Varicose veins, 171
Virus pneumonia, child, 68
Visiting Nurse Association, 197, 200-201
Vitamin deficiency, 171-172
Vitamins, 39
Vomit, blood in, 68
Vomiting, 62, 84-85

W

Warts, 85
Water, 21-22
Weaning problems, 59
Weight, 83-84, 98, 104, 157, 244
Wet dreams, 101
Whitfield's Ointment, U.S.P., 58
Winter itch, 58
Whooping cough, 85
Women, middle-aged, 236-237, 240
Worms, 85-86
Worry, 172
Wound, stitches, 62
Wrinkles, 172-173
Wry neck, 173

X

X-rays, free, 198

Y

Y M C A, 189
Y M H A, 189
Young, married people, 236, 240
Y W C A, 189